Woman's Day®
WORD-FINDS™

Welcome to Woman's Day® Word-Finds. In each puzzle, look for the words in CAPITAL letters on the left-hand page, then find those words in the diagram on the right side. The hidden words are always in a straight line and may be read up, down, forwards, backwards, or diagonally. As you find each word, circle it in the diagram and mark it off the word list. Many words will overlap Remember, only capitalized words and phrases can be found in the diagram.

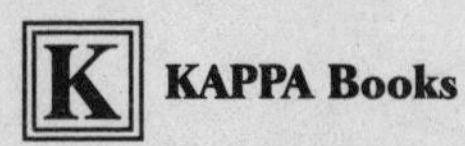

KAPPA Books

Visit us at www.kappapuzzles.com

1

Scrapbooking

ALBUMS
BABY
BEADS
CARDSTOCK
CRAFTS
EMBELLISHMENTS
FLOWERS
GLITTER
HOLIDAYS
JOURNALING
MEMORIES
PAGE PROTECTORS
PAPER
PHOTOS
PUNCHES
RIBBON
SCHOOL
SCISSORS
SCRAPBOOK
SENTIMENTS
SPORTS
STAMPS
STENCILS
STICKERS
TAPE
TRAVEL
TRIM
WEDDINGS

S	R	O	T	C	E	T	O	R	P	E	G	A	P
T	E	T	Z	J	S	T	A	M	P	S	N	R	Y
N	T	N	U	S	R	S	R	O	S	S	I	C	S
E	T	S	T	I	C	K	E	R	S	B	L	Y	N
M	I	S	M	I	D	H	E	S	B	P	A	H	S
H	L	E	L	N	M	W	O	O	N	D	N	C	S
S	G	I	H	I	O	E	N	O	I	B	R	A	T
I	P	R	P	L	C	A	N	L	L	A	U	F	F
L	H	O	F	U	L	N	O	T	P	B	O	T	A
L	O	M	R	B	N	H	E	B	S	Y	J	R	R
E	T	E	U	T	K	C	O	T	S	D	R	A	C
B	O	M	A	Z	S	O	H	N	S	T	A	V	W
M	S	P	S	R	K	N	R	E	P	A	P	E	H
E	E	W	E	D	D	I	N	G	S	R	Z	L	B

2

Healthy Eating

BLUEBERRIES:

May HELP

MEMORY and

BALANCE.

BROCCOLI:

PROVIDES

FIBER and

VITAMIN C.

GARLIC:

BLOCKS

PARASITES

that CAUSE

DISEASE.

GREEN

NUTS:

REDUCE the

LEVEL of

CHOLESTEROL.

OATS:

LOWER

BLOOD

PRESSURE.

SALMON:

May help PREVENT

HEART disease.

SPINACH:

SUPPLIES

the BODY

with IRON

and B VITAMINS.

W	I	C	B	L	O	O	D	X	Z	B	K	N	U
C	C	B	M	R	Y	N	O	M	L	A	S	O	R
N	N	H	L	R	O	E	R	U	S	S	E	R	P
B	Z	I	O	O	E	C	E	Q	T	U	S	I	E
N	R	M	M	L	C	B	C	T	U	P	J	F	S
T	E	S	G	A	E	K	I	O	N	P	C	E	A
M	W	E	N	R	T	S	S	F	L	L	D	Q	E
C	O	T	R	B	V	I	T	A	M	I	N	S	S
A	L	I	H	G	H	C	V	E	V	E	M	P	I
U	E	S	Z	E	I	H	C	O	R	S	B	I	D
S	D	A	A	L	L	U	R	Y	D	O	B	N	O
E	N	R	R	N	D	P	L	E	V	E	L	A	H
F	T	A	G	E	C	N	A	L	A	B	T	C	V
G	G	P	R	E	V	E	N	T	V	S	K	H	S

3

Orchids

ASIA

AUSTRALIA

Pollinated by BATS

BEAUTY

Pollinated by BIRDS

BOUQUET

Tree BRANCHES

CHRISTMAS orchid

Varied COLORS

CORSAGE

DOVE orchid

FRAGRANCE

GIFT

Pollinated by INSECTS

LADY'S slipper

MEXICO

ORCHIDACEAE (family)

PERENNIAL

Large central PETAL

POPULAR

RAINY climates

SCORPION orchid

2000 SPECIES

SPECKLED

STAR orchid

STREAKED orchid

TROPICS

TRUNKS of trees

VANILLA orchid

WILDFLOWER

Y	C	R	G	R	F	N	B	S	R	O	L	O	C
S	O	A	I	L	A	R	T	S	U	A	R	R	T
E	R	I	F	S	A	L	A	B	A	T	S	A	Y
I	S	N	T	N	T	M	U	G	I	O	H	T	L
C	A	Y	C	E	T	R	D	P	R	R	U	S	A
E	G	H	G	S	U	A	E	C	O	A	D	Z	I
P	E	D	I	D	L	Q	H	A	E	P	N	S	N
S	I	R	E	L	S	I	U	B	K	W	B	C	N
A	H	W	I	L	D	F	L	O	W	E	R	O	E
C	O	N	A	A	K	A	X	M	B	A	D	R	R
L	A	D	C	S	T	C	E	S	N	I	S	P	E
V	Y	E	I	E	O	M	E	X	I	C	O	I	P
S	A	T	P	F	T	R	O	P	I	C	S	O	A
E	V	O	D	T	R	U	N	K	S	S	Y	N	J

4

Breakfast Foods

BANANAS

BLUEBERRY muffin

CANTALOUPE

CHEESE DANISH

Hot CHOCOLATE

CREAM CHEESE

DIET SHAKE

GRANOLA

HAM AND EGGS

HARD-BOILED egg

HOME fries

JELLY

LOX

MARGARINE

MARMALADE

MILK

PANCAKES

Cold PIZZA

SAUSAGE

SCRAMBLED eggs

SCRAPPLE

SHREDDED wheat

STEAK

STRAWBERRIES

Maple SYRUP

Smoked WHITEFISH

Y	R	R	E	B	E	U	L	B	B	B	D	W	R
P	C	C	H	O	C	O	L	A	T	E	E	Q	S
S	I	A	C	S	X	O	N	N	D	C	L	M	H
U	T	Z	N	B	I	A	K	A	P	R	B	A	R
V	E	R	Z	T	N	F	L	L	R	E	M	R	E
E	G	X	A	A	A	A	E	E	I	A	A	G	D
L	A	R	S	W	M	L	K	T	N	M	R	A	D
P	S	H	A	R	B	A	O	D	I	C	C	R	E
P	U	O	A	N	H	E	E	U	J	H	S	I	D
A	A	M	S	S	O	G	R	Q	P	E	W	N	P
R	S	E	T	A	G	L	J	R	H	E	L	E	U
C	H	E	E	S	E	D	A	N	I	S	H	L	R
S	I	H	A	R	D	B	O	I	L	E	D	L	Y
D	D	S	K	P	A	N	C	A	K	E	S	L	S

5

Seasoned Green Beans

3 1/2 CUPS FRESH or FROZEN GREEN BEANS;
2 tbsp. BUTTER or MARGARINE, MELTED;
1/4 to 1/2 tsp. SEASONED SALT;
1/8 tsp. EACH GARLIC powder and ONION POWDER.
PLACE beans In STEAMER BASKET; place in SAUCEPAN over 1 inch WATER.

BRING to BOIL, COVER and STEAM FOR 7-8 MINUTES or UNTIL CRISP-TENDER.
In SMALL BOWL COMBINE REST of INGREDIENTS.
DRAIN beans; ADD mixture and TOSS to COAT.
4 SERVINGS

D	C	R	Q	B	R	I	N	G	B	E	G	E	E
P	D	E	T	L	E	M	S	A	L	T	A	O	C
S	D	V	N	O	G	A	R	L	I	C	R	B	A
I	E	O	I	I	U	F	N	R	H	E	U	O	L
R	N	C	N	C	B	I	E	S	D	T	N	X	P
C	O	G	E	P	A	M	Z	W	T	Q	T	E	R
M	S	P	R	R	A	N	O	E	C	L	I	O	B
I	A	G	D	E	O	P	R	C	A	U	L	B	O
N	E	A	T	I	D	F	F	E	W	D	P	A	W
U	S	S	N	S	J	I	M	R	D	A	W	S	L
T	K	O	M	I	E	B	E	A	E	N	T	K	Z
E	M	A	R	G	A	R	I	N	E	S	E	E	S
S	L	T	A	N	E	E	R	G	T	T	H	T	R
L	O	O	S	G	N	I	V	R	E	S	S	O	T

6

Art Supplies

ACRYLIC paints
AIRBRUSH
BLENDERS
BRUSHES
CANVAS
CHARCOAL
CLAY
CRAYONS
EASEL
ERASER
GLITTER
GRAPHITE
INDIA INK
MANNEQUIN
MARKERS
OIL PAINTS
OIL PASTELS
PALETTE
PENCILS
PENS
RULER
SANDPAPER
SKETCH pads
STENCILS
Pastel STICKS
TORTILLON
TUBES
WATERCOLORS

I	R	I	Z	M	A	R	K	E	R	S	H	S	Q
N	I	U	Q	E	N	N	A	M	R	O	K	S	A
D	O	S	L	P	L	S	T	E	N	C	I	L	S
I	Y	L	C	E	E	E	D	R	I	B	O	I	G
A	R	I	L	O	R	N	T	T	E	I	K	C	L
I	E	C	A	I	E	O	S	I	L	S	R	A	I
N	P	N	Y	L	T	L	B	P	H	A	A	I	T
K	A	E	B	P	S	R	A	T	Y	P	F	R	T
S	P	P	L	A	U	I	O	O	U	Q	A	B	E
K	D	D	V	S	N	R	N	T	C	B	N	R	R
E	N	N	H	T	L	S	Z	V	F	R	E	U	G
T	A	E	S	E	T	T	E	L	A	P	A	S	A
C	S	R	O	L	O	C	R	E	T	A	W	H	N
H	J	E	A	S	E	L	A	C	R	Y	L	I	C

Cherries

BING
CANNED
COBBLER
COOKING
DARK RED
DELICATE
ENDOCARP
EXOCARP
FAT FREE
FIRM
FRESH
FROZEN
HEART-SHAPED
MAHOGANY red
MONTMORENCY
MORELLO
OBLONG
PIES
PIT
RECIPES
REFRIGERATE
ROUND
ROYAL ANN
SALADS
SAUCES
SHINY
SMOOTH
SOUR
STEM
SWEET
TARTS
VITAMIN C
YELLOW

H	S	D	D	R	U	O	S	V	R	F	R	P	M
Y	T	S	E	E	T	A	I	E	R	S	O	G	A
N	E	O	T	P	L	T	C	E	A	T	Y	N	H
I	M	I	O	A	A	I	S	U	U	R	A	I	O
H	P	R	D	M	P	H	C	C	R	A	L	K	G
S	R	S	I	E	S	E	S	A	A	T	A	O	A
O	A	N	S	F	S	V	M	T	T	N	N	O	N
B	C	E	M	O	N	T	M	O	R	E	N	C	Y
L	O	R	E	F	R	I	G	E	R	A	T	E	S
O	X	E	Y	R	S	G	L	S	J	E	E	I	D
N	E	Z	O	R	F	B	G	X	W	T	L	H	N
G	N	I	B	C	B	T	A	P	I	E	S	L	U
Y	E	L	L	O	W	D	A	R	K	R	E	D	O
P	R	A	C	O	D	N	E	F	H	T	D	T	R

8 Blogging from Home

ADVICE
ARTICLES
CHILDCARE
CHILDREN
DECORATIONS
DISCUSSIONS
FORMAT
GUIDE
HINTS
HOSTING
IDEAS
INTERNET
ISSUES
LINKS
Time MANAGEMENT
PARENTING
PERSONAL blog
PHOTOS
POSTINGS
PRODUCTS
RECIPES
RESEARCH
REVIEWS
WEBSITE

S O U K P A R T I C L E S J
I S S U E S R L Q O N T Z J
X K C S T T S E P I C E R H
J N H S N O I S S U C S I D
A I I W E O M S D E C G Z S
P L L E M J I O B H A I D O
E A D I E A R T I E D R P T
R D R V G P S L A R W O C O
S V E E A T D T O R S V X H
O I N R N C X G A T O E Z P
N C M I A T U E I M V C Z C
A E H R M I I N T E R N E T
L V E K D U G N I T S O H D
K I D E A S L J G W E V F E

9

Sushi

BAMBOO shoots
CHIRASHI sushi
COLORFUL
EGGS
FILLING
FISH
FRESH
FUKIN
GARI
JAPANESE
MAKI
MOLD
NETA
OSHI
PACKING
PRESENTATION
PRESSED
RAW fish
RED MEAT
RICE
SCATTERED
SEAFOOD
SEAWEED
SHOYA
SURIMI
THICK ROLLS
THIN ROLLS
TOFU
TOPPINGS
VEGETABLES
WASABI
WRAPPED

N	O	I	T	A	T	N	E	S	E	R	P	W	T
S	I	T	H	D	L	O	M	E	S	U	C	X	I
S	G	K	O	S	E	C	O	L	O	R	F	U	L
L	N	G	U	P	O	R	L	B	J	C	H	O	E
L	I	N	E	F	P	O	E	A	U	H	S	C	T
O	K	I	G	A	R	I	P	T	S	I	I	T	P
R	C	L	W	K	Z	A	N	E	T	R	F	R	D
N	A	L	C	S	N	A	R	G	F	A	E	N	S
I	P	I	L	E	E	F	R	E	S	S	C	U	O
H	H	F	S	R	A	A	A	V	S	H	R	S	O
T	D	E	P	P	A	R	W	E	Z	I	O	I	B
J	S	E	A	F	O	O	D	E	M	A	K	Y	M
P	R	P	W	A	S	A	B	I	E	A	V	B	A
Z	Q	A	V	N	E	T	A	E	M	D	E	R	B

10

Washers

AGITATOR
APPLIANCE
BASKET
CAPACITY
CENTRIFUGAL force
CYCLES
DELICATE
DIALS
DISPENSERS
DURABLE
ENERGY
FRONT-LOAD washer
HIGH-SPEED
LINT filter
LOADED
PORCELAIN
RINSES
SETTINGS
SPIN
STACKABLE
Stainless STEEL
TEMPERATURE
TIMER
TOP-LOAD washer
TOUCH PANEL
TUB
UNBALANCED
WASHES

L	A	G	U	F	I	R	T	N	E	C	R	M	D
E	S	E	L	C	Y	C	T	I	M	E	R	D	E
C	X	S	S	T	A	C	K	A	B	L	E	R	C
N	C	N	R	D	T	P	Y	L	S	L	U	E	N
A	K	H	M	E	E	I	A	E	I	T	G	L	A
I	W	I	S	R	S	D	S	C	A	N	E	B	L
L	S	G	E	E	O	N	A	R	I	N	T	A	A
P	E	H	H	N	I	T	E	O	A	T	B	R	B
P	T	S	S	R	E	P	A	P	L	A	Y	U	N
A	T	P	A	B	M	R	H	T	S	E	T	D	U
P	I	E	W	E	L	C	G	K	I	I	E	W	G
N	N	E	T	S	U	G	E	Y	A	G	D	T	B
S	G	D	A	O	L	T	N	O	R	F	A	J	S
R	S	G	T	O	P	L	O	A	D	I	A	L	S

Pickles

BARREL
BRINE
CANDIED
CHIPS
CHUNKS
CRISP
CRUNCHY
CUCUMBER
CURED
DILL
FAT FREE
FERMENTED
FRESH pack
GHERKIN
GREEN
HALVED
JARS
KOSHER
PROCESSED
RELISH
SALADS
SALTY
SEASONINGS
SEEDS
SKIN
SLICES
SOUR
SPEARS
SWEET
VINE
WHOLE
ZESTY

S	R	A	J	C	L	S	H	D	S	S	D	P	H
D	P	Y	H	S	B	E	K	G	E	K	K	S	T
E	H	I	H	A	L	N	N	N	S	R	E	I	I
E	P	P	R	C	D	I	L	L	U	R	U	R	N
S	H	R	R	T	N	V	C	O	F	H	M	C	E
A	E	A	R	O	S	U	S	E	K	S	C	U	E
L	Z	X	S	V	C	S	R	R	S	A	A	C	R
A	F	A	T	F	R	E	E	C	N	L	N	U	G
D	E	V	L	A	H	L	S	D	Q	T	I	M	S
S	K	B	E	Q	I	D	I	S	I	Y	K	B	F
D	W	P	R	S	D	E	T	N	E	M	R	E	F
W	S	E	H	I	D	P	N	G	V	D	E	R	B
Y	T	S	E	Z	N	D	S	K	O	S	H	E	R
T	P	Y	E	T	W	E	L	O	H	W	G	E	R

Pet Care

ADOPTION
AQUARIUM
BATHS
BIRDS
CATS
COLLAR
CRATES
DOGS
EXERCISE
EXOTIC pets
FISH
FOOD
FRESH air
HARD work
Pet INSURANCE
LEASH
MEDICINE
OBEDIENCE school
PET-PROOFING
RESCUE
SHOTS
TOYS
TRAINING
TREATS
VETERINARIAN
WALKS
WASH
WATER

B	N	T	R	S	C	C	I	T	O	X	E	F	C
B	A	Q	O	O	K	E	V	D	T	G	N	O	G
R	I	O	L	Y	P	L	S	R	N	Q	I	R	E
B	R	L	E	A	S	H	A	I	K	B	C	E	C
I	A	G	S	G	D	I	F	W	C	N	I	T	N
R	N	N	O	T	N	O	T	S	P	R	D	A	E
D	I	D	S	I	O	A	O	R	K	X	E	W	I
S	R	W	N	R	F	H	Q	F	E	R	M	X	D
P	E	G	P	S	I	N	S	U	R	A	N	C	E
M	T	T	A	E	S	E	C	K	A	G	T	B	B
G	E	R	D	T	H	S	E	R	F	R	A	S	O
P	V	R	M	A	E	A	D	O	P	T	I	O	N
Q	A	G	I	R	A	U	W	U	H	Y	L	U	W
H	S	A	W	C	Y	I	V	S	T	A	C	E	M

Meatballs

BEEF
BREAD CRUMBS
BROWN
CHICKEN
CHOP
COVER
Hors D'OEUVRE
EGG
ENTREE
FLOUR
FORM
FRYING pan
GERMANY
GRAVY
GROUND beef
MINCED
MIXED
OIL
ONION
PAPRIKA
Dried PARSLEY
PEPPER
PORK
ROLL
SALT
SIMMER
STIR
SWEDISH
TURKEY
VEAL
WATER
WORCESTERSHIRE sauce

B	E	Q	T	D	X	D	U	D	N	U	O	R	G
K	R	O	P	T	O	Y	M	H	J	N	W	U	Y
W	I	E	L	U	N	E	K	C	I	H	C	O	L
C	H	A	A	A	H	P	U	O	O	R	L	L	A
U	S	R	M	D	A	A	N	V	E	V	R	F	Z
E	R	R	I	R	C	P	G	M	R	E	E	N	A
G	E	E	N	T	N	R	M	N	T	E	R	R	F
G	T	E	C	Z	S	I	U	A	I	C	H	O	P
R	S	R	E	T	S	K	W	M	Q	Y	R	A	D
A	E	T	D	P	U	A	Y	M	B	M	R	R	K
V	C	N	N	W	O	R	B	I	P	S	P	F	V
Y	R	E	P	P	E	P	K	X	L	X	G	E	V
R	O	L	L	Z	P	W	I	E	R	I	A	E	J
S	W	E	D	I	S	H	Y	D	Y	L	O	B	H

14 Going Back to School

THINKING ABOUT ENROLLING in CLASSES? DON'T let your STRESSFUL LIFE DISSUADE you. EXPLAIN the TIME you will NEED to do your WORK with your FAMILY and how THEY can HELP you. COSTS are HIGHER than in the PAST, but AGAIN, don't be SCARED: FINANCIAL AID FOR ADULTS is AVAILABLE. ONLINE COURSES are an ALTERNATIVE if GETTING to a SCHOOL is DIFFICULT or UNREALISTIC.

S	S	E	S	S	A	L	C	U	H	U	E	T	C
K	C	D	V	I	D	E	L	Z	N	L	S	U	H
J	E	H	I	I	E	E	D	R	B	A	T	O	B
W	F	X	O	F	T	G	E	A	P	S	R	B	S
S	O	Y	P	O	F	A	L	N	U	T	E	A	C
E	N	R	O	L	L	I	N	G	O	S	S	L	A
S	A	X	K	I	A	B	C	R	E	O	S	A	R
R	G	I	S	V	H	I	G	U	E	C	F	I	E
U	A	T	A	I	O	N	N	T	L	T	U	C	D
O	I	H	G	N	I	K	N	I	H	T	L	N	G
C	N	H	L	T	X	O	R	O	F	D	I	A	H
R	E	I	T	A	D	U	L	T	S	W	Q	N	E
R	N	E	E	M	I	T	P	M	C	E	F	I	L
E	G	F	G	T	H	E	Y	L	I	M	A	F	P

15

Apple Brickle Dip

8 oz PACKAGE
CREAM
CHEESE,
SOFTENED;
1/2 cup PACKED
BROWN sugar;
1/4 cup SUGAR;
1 tsp. VANILLA
EXTRACT;
7 1/2 oz pkg. ALMOND
BRICKLE
CHIPS or
10 oz. ENGLISH
TOFFEE
BITS;
3 MEDIUM
TART
APPLES,
CUT
INTO
CHUNKS.
In MIXING
BOWL;
BEAT
first FOUR
INGREDIENTS.
FOLD IN
NEXT ingredient.
SERVE
WITH
THE
FRUIT.
REFRIGERATE
LEFTOVERS.

P	E	P	A	C	K	E	D	O	N	S	M	D	H
O	B	I	T	S	S	N	C	C	S	E	I	R	B
T	S	V	B	U	O	M	W	R	H	P	X	R	O
N	C	E	G	M	A	F	E	O	B	U	I	T	W
I	S	A	L	E	J	V	T	E	R	C	N	H	L
D	R	A	R	P	O	N	A	E	K	B	G	K	C
L	E	C	T	T	P	T	R	L	N	M	I	J	S
O	N	E	F	Z	X	A	E	S	E	E	H	C	H
F	G	E	H	D	Y	E	G	D	L	O	D	V	T
E	L	F	S	V	A	N	I	L	L	A	P	A	I
Z	I	F	E	T	I	U	R	F	O	U	R	F	W
Z	S	O	R	T	M	I	F	I	K	T	U	C	S
W	H	T	V	X	H	X	E	G	A	K	C	A	P
S	T	N	E	I	D	E	R	G	N	I	W	B	S

16 Mushroom-Thyme Gravy

2 tbsp. BUTTER;
1 SMALL onion,
CHOPPED;
8 oz. SLICED
MUSHROOMS;
2 cans TURKEY or
CHICKEN broth;
1/4 cup FLOUR;
1 1/2 tsp. FRESH
THYME, chopped.
MELT butter in
a LARGE
SAUCEPAN.
Add ONION and
COOK,
STIRRING
OCCASIONALLY,
6 MINUTES or
until TENDER.
POUR 1 can
BROTH into a
BOWL and
WHISK in flour
UNTIL
BLENDED. Stir in
OTHER
CAN OF broth
and thyme.
BRING to a
BOIL.
REDUCE
HEAT and
SIMMER 7 min.
until SLIGHTLY
THICKENED.

B	T	Q	R	B	F	G	V	U	N	T	I	L	P
Y	M	S	C	D	B	R	O	T	H	V	N	A	O
Y	E	K	R	U	T	E	E	L	W	O	B	R	U
B	L	E	N	D	E	D	S	S	I	B	S	G	R
R	T	L	S	M	S	U	M	N	H	T	Y	E	E
I	S	M	A	L	L	C	O	W	I	E	D	X	H
N	H	Q	I	N	I	E	O	R	K	N	A	T	T
G	D	C	N	V	O	G	R	R	E	S	G	T	O
D	E	N	E	K	C	I	H	T	E	T	I	C	M
D	P	F	K	H	N	E	S	T	F	M	T	H	R
L	P	B	C	G	M	K	U	A	L	O	M	U	W
I	O	Y	I	Y	O	N	M	D	C	Y	N	I	B
O	H	C	H	O	I	N	A	P	E	C	U	A	S
B	C	T	C	M	R	U	O	L	F	Y	O	Y	C

17

Spice Rack

ALLSPICE
ANISE
BASIL
BAY LEAVES
CARAWAY
CARDAMOM
CHERVIL
CHIVES
CINNAMON
DILL
GARLIC
GINGER
GREEN pepper
HORSERADISH
JALAPENO
MACE
MARJORAM
MUSTARD
NUTMEG
ONION
PARSLEY
PEPPER CORN
PIMENTO
ROSEMARY
SAGE
SAVORY
TARRAGON
TUMERIC
VANILLA

N	E	C	I	N	N	A	M	O	N	O	I	N	O
E	Y	Y	R	O	V	A	S	N	U	T	M	E	G
E	A	H	H	Z	R	A	L	L	I	N	A	V	C
R	W	N	R	O	C	R	E	P	P	E	P	M	A
G	A	Z	J	K	R	C	I	R	E	M	U	T	R
P	R	R	A	N	I	S	E	N	S	I	L	R	D
M	A	O	N	P	V	C	E	O	E	P	E	E	A
M	C	R	S	O	H	L	J	R	V	G	S	G	M
Z	U	L	S	E	G	J	A	L	A	P	E	N	O
A	L	S	R	L	M	A	B	S	E	D	V	I	M
A	P	V	T	A	E	A	R	R	L	I	I	G	X
T	I	A	C	A	S	Y	R	R	Y	L	H	S	R
L	G	E	A	I	R	U	S	Y	A	L	C	F	H
G	A	R	L	I	C	D	A	F	B	T	L	G	Q

18

Dishwashers

ADJUSTABLE
BASKET
CONTROLS
CYCLES
Time DELAY
DETERGENT
DISHES
DOOR
DRAWER
DRYER
EFFICIENCY
ENERGY saving
EXTERIOR
EXTRA rinse
FLAT-FRONT
GLASSES
HIDDEN knobs
INSULATION
LEADING
MULTIPLE arms
OPTIONS
PLASTIC
POTS and pans
PUMP
RACKS
SOAP
SPRAY arms
STAINLESS steel
TEMPERATURE
TIMER
UTENSILS
WASH
WATER saving

W	T	E	K	S	A	B	W	S	P	R	A	Y	R
E	A	X	P	S	L	I	S	N	E	T	U	C	P
N	N	T	R	M	D	E	T	E	R	G	E	N	T
N	D	E	E	R	U	T	A	R	E	P	M	E	T
R	O	R	R	R	M	P	I	T	T	H	L	I	G
A	O	I	Y	G	N	U	N	A	I	B	M	C	H
C	H	O	T	E	Y	O	L	R	A	E	Z	I	C
K	O	R	D	A	R	G	E	T	R	C	D	F	I
S	C	N	O	F	L	W	S	X	I	D	D	F	T
F	Y	W	T	A	A	U	S	E	E	P	E	E	S
R	C	A	S	R	J	T	S	N	V	Z	L	O	A
C	L	S	D	D	O	U	G	N	I	D	A	E	L
F	E	H	A	P	T	L	V	E	I	P	Y	Z	P
S	S	D	I	S	H	E	S	N	O	I	T	P	O

19

Croquet

BALKLINES
BISQUE (free turn)
BONUS stroke
CARRYING case
COLORED balls
COURSE
DOUBLE diamond
EASY to learn
FAMILY game
GOLF croquet
GRASS court
HOOPS
LAWN
MALLET
MIXED-GENDER
championship
OPPONENT
OUTDOORS
PARTNERS
PLASTIC ball
RULES
SINGLES
STAKES
STRIPES
STROKES
SWING
TOURNAMENTS
Take TURNS
WICKETS
WOODEN mallet
YARD LINE

E	P	F	A	J	E	U	Q	S	I	B	B	B	C
X	H	O	O	P	S	R	E	N	T	R	A	P	F
L	D	C	Y	A	S	K	N	W	A	L	S	A	S
Y	E	O	O	A	O	R	C	Y	K	I	M	T	S
B	R	U	U	R	R	E	R	L	N	I	E	N	N
O	O	R	T	B	G	D	I	G	L	K	R	E	E
N	L	S	D	X	L	N	L	Y	C	U	U	N	D
U	O	E	O	T	E	E	I	I	T	Q	L	O	O
S	C	T	O	S	S	G	W	Y	N	O	E	P	O
G	E	O	R	Y	D	D	U	X	R	E	S	P	W
F	R	K	S	T	N	E	M	A	N	R	U	O	T
L	C	A	A	W	R	X	C	I	T	S	A	L	P
O	E	J	S	T	R	I	P	E	S	U	A	C	W
G	N	I	W	S	S	M	A	L	L	E	T	F	F

20

Coffee

BEANS
BERRY
BEVERAGE
BREWED
CAFFEINE
CAPPUCCINO
CLIMATE
COFFEEHOUSE
CREAM
DRINK
ESPRESSO
ETHIOPIA
FILTERS
GROUND
HARVESTED
HOT MILK
INSTANT
ITALY
JAVA
MILD
MOCHA
PICKED
ROASTED
RUBIACEAE family
SACCHARIN
STIMULANT
TURKEY

S	Z	L	B	C	A	P	P	U	C	C	I	N	O
Y	D	E	K	C	I	P	G	R	O	U	N	D	B
R	E	E	T	E	N	I	E	F	F	A	C	M	R
R	M	K	T	A	P	I	F	F	B	T	B	I	N
E	E	O	R	S	M	E	R	E	N	E	E	L	N
B	S	E	C	U	E	I	F	A	V	H	A	D	U
F	P	W	A	H	T	V	L	E	H	T	N	E	M
I	R	K	O	A	A	U	R	C	N	C	S	T	U
L	E	U	L	V	M	A	O	A	A	N	C	S	M
T	S	Y	A	I	G	X	T	I	H	V	V	A	N
E	S	J	T	E	M	S	P	B	R	R	E	O	S
R	O	S	C	B	N	T	D	U	W	R	F	R	Z
S	V	K	N	I	R	D	O	R	C	T	U	L	Z
D	E	W	E	R	B	E	T	H	I	O	P	I	A

21

Organization Tips

CREATE a

LOST and

FOUND

BIN in your

HOME

WHERE you can

PUT ALL the

THINGS

THAT you

KNOW

BELONG to

SOMETHING

ELSE or a

SET — an

ELECTRONIC

DEVICE or

GAME

BOARD, for

EXAMPLE — but

CAN'T

REMEMBER where it

GOES.

ANOTHER bin

CONTAINING

ITEMS to be

FIXED when you

FIND the

TIME gets all of

THOSE

LITTLE

PROJECTS in one

PLACE.

C	B	T	E	S	D	T	B	D	E	E	H	G	D
I	O	K	L	W	A	E	I	E	S	C	A	N	T
N	A	N	T	H	H	O	X	V	L	M	U	Q	C
O	R	O	T	T	A	E	I	I	E	O	D	C	A
R	D	W	I	A	L	S	R	C	F	N	N	X	A
T	E	J	L	P	I	O	E	E	F	I	I	G	Y
C	F	O	M	R	V	N	S	O	H	S	F	B	P
E	Y	A	W	E	V	I	I	T	G	T	O	R	L
L	X	R	H	M	T	U	R	N	F	I	O	G	L
E	S	O	M	E	T	H	I	N	G	J	T	N	K
E	M	L	M	M	Q	H	G	H	E	B	D	D	A
E	X	S	A	B	T	E	E	C	A	L	P	H	S
Q	T	I	M	E	P	U	T	A	L	L	K	X	J
E	T	A	E	R	C	S	E	S	O	H	T	Q	Q

22 Salmon Steaks with Salsa

1 tbsp. BUTTER;
4 - 8 oz. salmon
STEAKS;
1/2 cup WHITE wine;
1/2 tsp. BLACK
pepper;
2 tbsp. FRESH
oregano;
4 SCALLIONS;
8 oz. RIPE tomatoes,
PEELED;
2 tbsp. OLIVE OIL;
1/2 tsp. SUGAR;
1 tbsp. tomato PASTE.
PREHEAT
OVEN to 275 degrees.
Butter a DISH,
place the SALMON
in it AND ADD
the WINE
and PEPPER.
COVER with
FOIL and
BAKE 15 minutes
until FISH
is just COOKED.
Put OREGANO
in a PROCESSOR and
chop FINELY.
ADD THE scallions,
TOMATOES,
and remaining
INGREDIENTS.
PULSE to
ROUGHLY chop.
SERVE the
salmon COLD
with the SALSA,
and GARNISH
with PARSLEY.

R	E	T	T	U	B	H	O	O	K	H	H	A	R
E	I	P	A	R	S	L	E	Y	D	C	S	R	N
R	T	P	F	O	I	L	E	S	E	O	A	I	S
O	S	A	E	V	D	T	S	F	L	V	L	L	D
U	N	T	E	T	I	D	I	T	E	E	M	I	B
G	O	O	N	H	O	N	A	G	E	R	O	E	A
H	I	C	W	E	E	M	D	D	P	A	N	J	K
L	L	O	T	L	I	R	A	J	N	I	K	G	E
Y	L	O	Y	F	L	D	P	T	W	A	A	S	P
F	A	K	R	O	S	S	E	C	O	R	P	A	D
I	C	E	P	E	P	P	E	R	N	E	S	L	L
S	S	D	R	A	G	U	S	I	G	T	S	S	O
H	H	V	P	P	U	L	S	E	E	N	G	A	C
N	E	V	O	X	E	H	T	D	D	A	I	S	V

23

Reducing Energy

CEILING FANS use LITTLE ENERGY. WHEN you HAVE an AIR CONDITIONER on, TURN IT to a LOWER SETTING and LET THE fan PROPEL COOL air. REPLACE or CLEAN air conditioner FILTERS REGULARLY THROUGHOUT the SUMMER. VACUUM the COILS at the BACK and BOTTOM of your FRIDGE or FREEZER to REMOVE DUST and DEBRIS and INCREASE EFFICIENCY.

A	T	R	Q	R	F	M	O	T	T	O	B	Y	M
N	F	S	E	F	F	I	C	I	E	N	C	Y	J
A	I	W	L	N	F	A	L	G	L	D	G	L	A
E	O	O	S	R	O	Q	N	T	U	R	M	R	Z
L	O	G	I	R	F	I	B	S	E	K	C	A	B
C	B	D	R	G	L	O	T	N	U	R	R	L	G
X	G	V	B	I	N	D	E	I	E	M	S	U	D
E	O	A	E	F	C	I	N	V	D	H	M	G	I
L	L	C	D	R	P	C	T	T	O	N	W	E	O
T	E	U	J	E	R	A	H	T	U	M	O	R	R
T	T	U	B	E	C	A	L	P	E	R	E	C	S
I	T	M	A	Z	V	C	O	I	L	S	N	R	L
L	H	S	L	E	P	O	R	P	H	H	A	I	R
J	E	T	H	R	O	U	G	H	O	U	T	U	T

24

Pot Holders

APPLIQUED
BIAS TAPE
COLORFUL
COTTON
CROCHETED
DECORATIVE
DENIM
FABRIC
FLAT
MITT
PADDING
PAN GRABBER
PLAIN
PRINTS
PROTECTION
QUILTED
RECTANGLE
Heat RESISTANT
ROUND
SAFETY
SETS
SHAPES
SILICONE
TEFLON
TERRY CLOTH
THICK
TRIM
WASHABLE
WOVEN

R	E	B	B	A	R	G	N	A	P	L	A	I	N
M	O	H	R	C	O	L	O	R	F	U	L	S	N
C	H	U	D	E	U	Q	I	L	P	P	A	O	R
R	S	T	N	I	R	P	T	H	C	Z	T	T	F
W	E	S	O	D	F	K	C	R	R	T	D	E	N
B	A	S	M	L	C	E	E	N	O	E	E	F	V
I	Q	S	I	I	C	C	T	C	C	O	N	L	K
A	Z	U	H	S	T	Y	O	O	H	M	O	O	G
S	D	T	I	A	T	T	R	V	E	G	C	N	C
T	X	E	N	L	B	A	P	R	T	K	I	E	I
A	F	G	N	M	T	L	N	S	E	D	L	V	R
P	L	E	I	I	G	E	E	T	D	T	I	O	B
E	A	R	V	V	M	T	D	A	X	B	S	W	A
Y	T	E	F	A	S	E	P	A	H	S	N	Q	F

25

Fried Beans

BACON
BROWN
BUTTER
CHUNKY
CLOVES
COOK
CRUMBLE
DISH
DOLLOP
ENCHILADA
FLAVOR
FRAGRANT
GARLIC
LENTILS
MASH
MEXICAN
OLIVE OIL
ONIONS
PEPPER
PUREE
SALSA
SALT
SIMMER
SKILLET
SPICY
SPRINKLE
STIR
TACO
TASTY
TEXTURE
TORTILLAS
TOSTADA

Y	T	E	L	L	I	K	S	P	O	C	A	T	F
T	K	K	N	K	M	P	Y	S	E	G	F	F	L
S	I	N	A	C	I	X	E	M	E	P	P	N	A
A	M	G	U	C	H	V	L	R	T	U	P	S	V
T	L	A	Y	H	O	I	U	J	R	T	L	E	O
S	U	R	S	L	C	T	L	E	S	A	L	T	R
P	L	L	C	H	X	T	E	A	S	E	R	N	U
O	L	I	V	E	O	I	L	L	D	E	E	A	A
L	H	C	T	S	S	L	K	K	B	A	T	R	J
U	S	B	T	N	I	T	N	O	R	M	T	G	M
S	I	A	A	T	E	R	I	N	O	N	U	A	W
K	D	V	R	C	I	L	R	R	W	C	B	R	V
A	D	O	L	L	O	P	P	N	N	M	P	F	C
N	T	O	N	I	O	N	S	I	M	M	E	R	F

26

Planting Pots

ANTIQUED
CLAY
COATING
COLORFUL
CONCRETE
COPPER-PLATED
CRACKS
DRAINAGE
DURABLE
FADE
FIBERGLASS
FISHBOWL
FLOWERS
FRONT DOOR
GARDEN
HERBS
LACQUER
METAL
MODERNIST
PEDESTAL
PLANTS
PORCH
ROCKS
ROUND
STEEL
STEPS
TERRA COTTA
TREES
URNS
VEGETABLES
WALKWAY

N	J	R	H	F	M	U	R	N	S	B	R	E	H
E	B	O	G	I	M	O	W	A	L	K	W	A	Y
D	P	O	N	B	S	E	D	Q	V	Y	C	V	R
R	E	D	I	E	E	E	T	E	R	C	N	O	C
A	D	T	T	R	E	D	G	A	R	F	S	L	R
G	E	N	A	G	R	E	E	A	L	N	A	A	S
P	S	O	O	L	T	Q	C	U	N	C	I	D	P
L	T	R	C	A	P	K	F	D	Q	I	F	S	E
A	A	F	B	S	S	R	U	U	N	I	A	E	T
N	L	L	Y	S	O	R	E	S	L	U	T	R	S
T	E	A	P	L	A	R	J	P	A	E	O	N	D
S	L	W	O	B	H	S	I	F	P	T	E	R	A
C	C	C	L	T	E	R	R	A	C	O	T	T	A
S	R	E	W	O	L	F	C	P	O	R	C	H	S

Apricots

BETA-CAROTENE
BRIGHT orange
CAKE
CANNED
DELICATE flavor
DRIED
FAT FREE
FIBER
FRAGRANT
FRESH
FROZEN
FRUIT
GOLDEN
LOW CALORIE
OBLATE
ORANGE
PACKED
PIES
PLUMP
PULPED
ROUNDED
ROYAL
RUDDY
SALADS
SKIN
SOFT FLESH
STONE
SWEET aroma
VITAMIN C
WHITISH spots
YELLOW

E	N	E	T	O	R	A	C	A	T	E	B	S	T
I	E	E	D	N	T	H	S	I	T	I	H	W	D
R	Z	Q	D	I	A	D	F	A	T	F	R	E	E
O	O	T	U	L	A	R	C	E	O	L	I	E	N
L	R	R	E	L	O	I	G	O	Q	R	B	T	N
A	F	N	A	Y	L	G	B	A	D	S	K	O	A
C	T	S	A	E	R	L	M	P	R	O	N	V	C
W	A	L	D	S	A	O	Z	P	P	F	I	O	E
O	F	K	U	T	P	M	U	L	P	T	K	I	G
L	Y	I	E	O	H	L	T	N	A	F	S	V	N
T	L	E	B	N	P	G	D	M	D	L	J	E	A
W	O	L	L	E	Y	I	I	F	R	E	S	H	R
R	U	D	D	Y	R	N	E	R	P	S	D	G	O
G	C	D	E	K	C	A	P	S	B	H	H	D	C

28 Swimsuits

ADJUSTABLE
BANDEAU TOP
BELTED
BIKINI
COLORFUL
EMPIRE waist
FLATTERS
FRENCH bottom
HALTER top
HIGH-CUT
HIGH-WAISTED
LYCRA
MAILLOT
ONE-PIECE
PATTERNED
PIPING
PRINCESS seams
PRINT
SKIRTED
SPORTY
STRAPLESS
SUPPORT
TANKINI
TRIM
TWO-PIECE
V-NECK
WRAP SUIT

E N Y E V R D U D E O D N D

E C P Y S Z E C E I P E N O

P P E O Z S T T T E R N M O

T P R I T S S E L P A R T S

R S I I P U I B E A S E Y D

O K P P N O A F B F H T H F

P I M R I T W E M I R T L R

P R E X S N H T D O A A U E

U T I U N I G B P N T P F N

S E J N G K I S K T A Q R C

E D Y H C K H I E Z P B O H

A M C E I E N R A R C Y L X

W U N N C I S M A I L L O T

T V I W R A P S U I T A C M

29

Ice Cream Ideas

BOWL
BUTTERFAT
CAKE
CARAMEL
CHOCOLATE
COCONUT
CONE
CUSTARD
DESSERT
EGGS
FLAVOR
Ice-cream FLOAT
FROZEN
FRUITS
GELATIN
HARDEN
INGREDIENTS
MACAROONS
MILK
MIXED
NUTS
PARFAIT
PASTEURIZED
SAUCE
SHERBET
SOFT
SPRINKLES
SPUMONE
STRAWBERRY
SUGAR
VANILLA
WHIPPED topping

E	A	D	R	A	T	S	U	C	F	K	L	I	M
G	N	L	Z	U	S	H	E	R	B	E	T	D	Z
G	D	U	L	S	U	G	A	R	M	K	A	B	S
S	A	C	T	I	A	F	R	A	P	A	F	P	T
T	T	A	H	S	N	U	R	N	X	C	R	D	I
R	S	N	O	O	R	A	C	A	M	I	E	R	U
A	T	R	E	B	C	O	V	E	N	P	T	W	R
W	G	R	O	I	C	O	M	K	P	W	T	S	F
B	E	W	E	O	D	F	L	I	V	Q	U	P	L
E	L	F	N	S	R	E	H	A	X	A	B	U	A
R	A	U	L	O	S	W	R	K	T	E	V	M	V
R	T	S	Z	O	V	E	L	G	F	E	D	O	O
Y	I	E	F	H	A	R	D	E	N	O	C	N	R
Z	N	T	P	A	S	T	E	U	R	I	Z	E	D

30

Architectural Styles

ART DECO
ART NOUVEAU
BYZANTINE
CLASSICAL
Arts and CRAFTS
ELIZABETHAN
EXPRESSIONIST
GEORGIAN
GOOGIE
GOTHIC
GREEK revival
HINDU
JACOBEAN
MEDIEVAL
NEOLITHIC
NORMAN
PALLADIAN
POSTMODERN
PRAIRIE style
RENAISSANCE
ROCOCO
ROMANESQUE
ROMANTIC
TUDOR
VICTORIAN

T	S	I	N	O	I	S	S	E	R	P	X	E	V
T	T	U	A	E	V	U	O	N	T	R	A	E	W
Z	F	P	H	M	P	R	C	R	R	G	C	P	G
U	A	R	T	D	E	C	O	O	K	N	M	O	L
P	R	A	E	B	V	D	M	C	A	A	T	S	A
A	C	I	B	E	U	A	I	S	O	H	J	T	C
L	J	R	A	T	N	H	S	E	I	C	J	M	I
L	A	I	Z	T	T	I	E	C	V	Q	O	O	S
A	C	E	I	I	A	H	T	N	A	A	C	D	S
D	O	C	L	N	G	K	I	N	A	T	L	E	A
I	B	O	E	U	Q	S	E	N	A	M	O	R	L
A	E	R	G	O	O	G	I	E	D	Z	R	N	C
N	A	I	R	O	T	C	I	V	R	U	Y	O	W
L	N	A	I	G	R	O	E	G	W	G	C	B	N

31 Roasted Fan-Shaped Potatoes

12 large BAKING
potatoes;
1/2 TSP. SALT;
1/2 cup BUTTER,
MELTED,
DIVIDED in half;
6 TBSP. DRY bread
CRUMBS;
6 tbsp. SHREDDED
PARMESAN.
Fan the POTATOES by
slicing THINLY,
but not ALL THE WAY
THROUGH,
LEAVING slices
ATTACHED at the
BOTTOM.
PLACE in
GREASED baking
DISH.
SPRINKLE
WITH SALT.
BRUSH with
1/4 CUP butter.
Bake UNCOVERED
at 425
degrees for 30
MINUTES.
REPEAT using
REST of butter
and BREAD
crumbs. BAKE
ANOTHER 20 min.
Sprinkle with CHEESE.
Bake 10-15 minutes
MORE.

P A R M E S A N R E P E A T
T L A S H T I W B O T T O M
X L A V S S B U T T E R G A
S T D C B R E A D L L R N D
V H S N E W T T K G E Z I H
D E R E V O C N U A A C K E
E W W E E R I Y S N V R A D
H A T S D R R E A O I U B E
C Y Y S P D D E T T N M R D
A U S S P E E S S H G B U I
T V P S T S E D S E I S S V
T N B L W R A I I R E N H I
A T E K A B D L I O H H L D
Y M H G U O R H T M B I C Y

32 Chipotle-Orange BBQ Meatballs

12 oz. LEAN
GROUND beef;
1/2 cup CRUSHED
TORTILLA chips;
1/2 cup CILANTRO;
1/3 cup SLICED
scallions;
1 LARGE egg;
1 tsp. EACH
CUMIN,
OREGANO, and
MINCED
GARLIC;
2/3 cup BARBECUE
sauce;
1 1/2 tsp. GRATED
orange ZEST;
1/4 cup ORANGE
juice.
MIX
BEEF,
CHIPS, 1/3 cup
CHOPPED cilantro
with EGG and
SPICES.
FORM into
30 BALLS.
COOK on a
SKILLET for
5-7 MINUTES
UNTIL
BROWNED. Add
SAUCE, zest,
REMAINING cilantro,
and JUICE to skillet
on low HEAT.
SERVE with
TOOTHPICKS.

T P S N V F D T E V R E S A

C O O K A H S E C I P S L A

F E E B I E D S T R G L H E

P D J A Z L L E D A I F T C

F N Q R C I L A N T R O A U

O U R B C H H E R W O G E A

R O R E G A N O T T O O H S

M R D C M G T G H R O R E L

I G E U A A E P A J A T B L

N Z P E U S I N B R U B L A

C X P G P C G N G N L I M B

E A O I K E L K I R T I C E

D E H S U R C M C N X N C E

I C C U M I N T U E G R A L

33

Seafood Appetizer

ANCHOVY paste
ASSORTMENT
BITE-SIZED
Crab CAKES
CANAPES
CLAMS
Crab CLAWS
Shrimp COCKTAIL
CRACKERS
DIPS
DRESSING
FINGER FOOD
FONDUE
LEMON shrimp
LOBSTER bites
MARINATE
MILD flavor
NIBBLE
OYSTER
PEPPER
RECIPES
ROLL-UP
SARDINES
SAUCY
SEASONED
SHELLFISH
SHRIMP
SPREAD
SUSHI
TOOTHPICKS

L	I	A	T	K	C	O	C	B	G	Z	E	R	Y
F	I	L	P	S	A	R	D	I	N	E	S	C	R
B	I	T	E	S	I	Z	E	D	I	H	U	Z	E
L	T	N	E	M	T	R	O	S	S	A	F	N	T
S	O	P	G	M	O	O	Y	I	S	S	O	I	S
E	O	B	U	E	I	N	F	A	E	P	N	B	Y
P	T	S	S	L	R	L	C	N	R	R	D	B	O
A	H	A	R	T	L	F	D	C	D	E	U	L	P
N	P	S	N	E	E	O	O	H	N	A	E	E	P
A	I	M	H	I	K	R	R	O	Z	D	P	S	S
C	C	S	U	R	R	C	S	V	D	P	U	W	M
K	K	K	K	G	I	A	A	Y	E	S	A	F	A
Z	S	P	I	D	E	M	M	R	H	L	Y	U	L
C	A	K	E	S	S	E	P	I	C	E	R	B	C

Scarves

ACCESSORY
BULKY
CASHMERE
CASUAL
CHENILLE
COLORFUL
COTTON
DESIGNER labels
DRAPE
DYED
EMBROIDERED
FLEECE
FURRY
HANDMADE
KNITTED
PLAID
PLAIN
POLYESTER
PROTECTION
REVERSIBLE
SHOULDER
SOFT
STRIPED
STYLE
TASSELS
THICK
TIED
TWISTY
WASHABLE
WEAR
WHIMSICAL
WRAP

D	E	S	I	G	N	E	R	P	B	D	E	R	S	
C	R	D	I	A	L	P	D	U	D	E	E	C	O	
F	L	E	E	C	E	D	L	A	Y	R	H	I	F	
H	W	Y	V	C	Y	K	E	C	M	E	A	N	T	
R	E	T	S	E	Y	L	O	P	N	D	O	P	L	
H	E	S	D	S	R	T	U	I	W	I	N	U	E	
D	R	I	A	S	T	S	L	H	T	O	F	A	S	
S	E	W	Z	O	J	L	I	C	N	R	N	T	H	
T	M	T	N	R	E	M	E	B	O	B	I	A	O	
Y	H	P	T	Y	S	T	Y	L	L	M	A	S	U	
L	S	I	A	I	O	K	O	R	G	E	L	S	L	
E	A	C	C	R	N	C	S	T	R	I	P	E	D	
P	C	A	P	K	W	K	C	A	S	U	A	L	E	
E	L	B	A	H	S	A	W	E	A	R	F	S	R	

35

Sunscreen Scene

ALOE VERA
ANTIOXIDANTS
APPLY
BASE
BLOCK
BRONZER
COVER
CURVES
FACE
Sun protection
FACTOR
FOAM
GELS
HYDRATING
INVISIBLE
LIGHT
LOTION
MATTE
MIST
MOIST
OIL-FREE
PROTECTION
SCENTED
SELF-TANNER
SKIN
SOOTHING
STICK
STROKE ON
TEXTURE
VITAMINS
WATERPROOF
WIPES

S Y K S Y T W K C O L B S F

T L V I N S C W I P E S M A

N P W G N I T A R D Y H A C

A P N A T O M O X A D S O T

D A P S T M T A B E C A F O

I R E O S E L F T A N N E R

X E L O C D R N E I S L I H

O V B T S B E P S T V E Z B

I E I H N C R E R U T X E T

T O S I S I V O R O A A G H

N L I N U R K M N F O E M G

A A V G U E B S I Z L F L I

R X N C O V E R R S E I S L

Q Y I N O I T O L F T R O M

36 Compost at Home

BINS
BIODEGRADE
BREAK DOWN
CARDBOARD
CHIPS
CLIPPINGS
CRUMBLE
DECOMPOSE
FLOWERS
FRUIT
GARDEN
GRASS
GROUND
LAYERING
LEAVES
MOIST
NUTRIENTS
ORGANIC
PEAT MOSS
PLANTS
REDUCES waste
SAWDUST
Peanut SHELLS
SHRED
Add to SOIL
STEMS
STRAW
STRIPS
TEA BAGS
TEXTURE
VEGETABLES

W	D	E	C	O	M	P	O	S	E	S	H	G	E
C	A	R	D	B	O	A	R	D	S	M	N	P	L
I	B	R	I	A	U	S	S	X	O	E	W	I	S
N	W	N	T	Q	R	G	H	I	G	T	O	M	L
A	S	E	Q	S	A	G	S	R	S	S	D	F	L
G	S	E	L	B	A	T	E	G	E	V	K	L	E
R	O	T	A	B	G	W	N	D	S	D	A	O	H
O	M	E	N	A	M	I	D	P	O	Y	E	W	S
P	T	L	R	E	P	U	I	U	E	I	R	E	F
L	A	D	E	P	I	R	R	R	S	G	B	R	S
A	E	T	I	A	T	R	I	C	D	T	U	S	S
N	P	L	P	S	V	N	T	C	H	I	P	S	A
T	C	Q	Z	Q	G	E	R	U	T	X	E	T	R
S	R	E	D	U	C	E	S	D	N	U	O	R	G

Salad Dressing

BASIL
BLUE CHEESE
BUTTERMILK
CAESAR
CANOLA OIL
CAPERS
CELERY SEEDS
CREAMY
DIPS
FRENCH
GARLIC
HONEY mustard
ITALIAN
LIME JUICE
MARJORAM
OLIVE OIL
ONION
OREGANO
PAPRIKA
PARSLEY
RANCH
SALT
SHALLOTS
SOUR CREAM
SPREADS
THYME
TOSS
VINEGAR

S	N	R	X	Z	S	B	N	Z	K	J	P	A	P
C	A	N	O	L	A	O	I	L	O	S	A	L	T
B	I	L	A	S	I	Y	I	I	L	K	E	O	S
T	L	Z	I	N	S	M	M	F	I	J	S	R	H
H	A	L	O	M	R	Y	J	A	V	S	E	N	A
Y	T	S	D	E	E	S	Y	R	E	L	E	C	L
M	I	Q	T	L	P	J	A	D	O	R	H	D	L
E	A	T	S	R	O	G	U	B	I	W	C	F	O
G	U	R	E	W	E	R	F	I	L	O	E	X	T
B	A	A	O	N	M	A	E	R	C	R	U	O	S
P	D	R	I	J	V	S	F	G	A	E	L	X	P
S	D	V	L	R	R	E	J	V	A	N	B	R	I
P	A	P	R	I	K	A	F	R	E	N	C	H	D
S	R	E	P	A	C	C	M	Y	E	N	O	H	K

38 Weekend at the Spa

ACTIVITIES
BOUTIQUE
COUNTRY
DE-STRESS
DRINKS
FACIAL
GALLERIES
GOLF
HIKING
HOLIDAY gift
HOT SPRINGS
MASSAGE
MEALS
MEDITATION
MUD BATH
PAMPER
PEDICURE
RELAXATION
RESORT
RESTAURANTS
RUBDOWN
SNACKS
SWIM
TRAVEL
VACATION
VIEW
VILLA
YOGA

S	L	K	H	I	K	I	N	G	B	C	R	Y	P
T	R	A	V	E	L	V	A	W	N	B	R	M	E
N	R	G	V	Q	R	L	K	O	O	T	U	S	D
A	V	O	Z	A	L	X	I	D	N	D	K	M	I
R	C	Y	S	E	C	T	H	U	B	C	B	E	C
U	Q	T	R	E	A	A	O	A	A	W	S	U	U
A	P	I	I	X	R	C	T	N	K	K	E	Q	R
T	E	A	A	V	F	H	S	I	N	H	H	I	E
S	B	L	M	A	I	W	P	I	O	F	O	T	V
E	E	L	C	P	I	T	R	I	S	N	L	U	L
R	S	I	C	M	E	D	I	T	A	T	I	O	N
F	A	V	Z	M	Y	R	N	E	I	R	D	B	G
L	J	M	A	S	S	A	G	E	S	L	A	E	M
Q	N	S	S	E	R	T	S	E	D	Q	Y	D	O

39

Memories in a Box

AUTOGRAPH
BIRTH certificate
BOWS
COLLECTIONS
CORAL
DANCE card
DRIVER'S license
GLOSSY
GREETING cards
GUEST book
HEIRLOOMS
INVITATION
JEWELRY
KEEPSAKES
LETTER
MASS card
MEMENTOS
MILESTONES
PHOTOS
REPORT card
SCRAPBOOK
SEA SHELLS
SOUVENIR
TICKET stubs
TOYS
TRINKETS
WEDDING photos

U	C	B	K	O	O	B	P	A	R	C	S	L	T
S	W	B	U	Q	R	K	U	W	T	S	E	U	G
F	R	G	R	E	E	T	I	N	G	M	A	S	S
C	H	E	P	K	O	P	H	O	T	O	S	E	W
W	O	O	V	G	E	G	R	Q	N	M	H	M	O
S	R	L	R	I	N	E	V	U	O	S	E	E	B
T	T	A	L	I	R	D	P	O	I	T	L	M	A
Y	P	E	D	E	A	D	L	S	T	I	L	E	L
H	R	D	K	N	C	R	X	Y	A	C	S	N	A
H	E	L	C	N	I	T	S	O	T	K	A	T	R
W	T	E	E	E	I	S	I	T	I	E	E	O	O
K	T	R	H	W	O	R	R	O	V	T	M	S	C
E	E	M	I	L	E	S	T	O	N	E	S	V	C
C	L	U	G	B	W	J	L	A	I	S	I	J	V

French Cuisine

AMUSE bouche
ANCHOVIES
APERITIF
ARTICHOKE
ASPARAGUS
AXOA
BREAD
CAULIFLOWER
GARBURE
GARLIC
GAUDES
MATEFAIM
MATELOTE
MUSHROOMS
OLIVES
PAN BAGNAT
PATE
PETITS POIS
PORT
POT-AU-FEU
RABBIT
RACLETTE
RATATOUILLE
ROAST
SAUCE
SCALLOPS
STEW
STRAWBERRY
TOMATO

P F Y P R E M I A F E T A M
A I R S O E R C I L R A G W
T T R O E R F U L P A X M Y
E I E E A D T I B B A R U T
S R B A W S U G A R A P S A
U E W B N O T A V S A A H N
M P A A T C L M G S R G R G
A A R A Q S H F P T O A O A
P E T I T S P O I S C E O B
T A S E E S L C V L T C M N
R A W V L L H A E I U U S A
M R I X A O X T B R E A D P
Q L N C K O T A M O T S C A
O T S E A E U E F U A T O P

41

Pick a Planner

ACTIVITIES
AGENDA
APPOINTMENTS
CALENDAR
COMMITMENTS
DIGITAL assistant
E-MAIL addresses
HIGHLIGHT
Pen HOLDER
LISTS
MONTHLY planner
ORGANIZER
PAGES
PERSONALIZED
PHONE numbers
PORTFOLIO
PRIORITIZE
ROUTINES
SCHEDULE
SPACE
SPIRAL
STURDY
SYNCHRONIZED
SYSTEMIZE
TIME management
Keep TRACK
WRITE

L	I	S	T	S	Q	C	A	L	E	N	D	A	R
V	A	A	P	P	O	I	N	T	M	E	N	T	S
A	D	S	L	I	A	M	E	H	Z	G	R	E	W
D	C	E	C	M	R	E	Z	I	N	A	G	R	O
N	O	T	Z	H	T	A	L	K	C	A	P	H	I
E	M	R	I	I	E	A	L	K	P	R	I	M	L
G	M	L	R	V	N	D	H	L	I	G	O	R	O
A	I	W	A	O	I	O	U	O	H	N	S	O	F
E	T	E	S	T	L	T	R	L	T	N	T	U	T
C	M	R	N	D	I	I	I	H	E	K	U	T	R
A	E	I	E	O	T	G	L	E	C	R	R	I	O
P	N	R	T	I	H	Y	I	V	S	N	D	N	P
S	T	N	Z	T	F	P	E	D	S	T	Y	E	Y
R	S	E	Z	I	M	E	T	S	Y	S	H	S	Y

42 Mozzarella Cheese

AFFUMICATA
APPETIZERS
Mozzarella BALLS
BOCCONCINI
BRINE
CALCIUM
COOKING
CREAMY
CURD
DRIED
FIRM
FLAVOR
FRESH
GOAT milk
ITALIAN
MELTS
MILD
MILK
PASTA
PIZZA
RINDLESS
RUBBERY
SALADS
SALTED
SCAMORZA
SEMI-SOFT
SHREDDED
SMOKED
STRING cheese
TEXTURE
WHEY
WHITE
WHOLE milk

D	C	N	A	I	L	A	T	I	D	Q	N	R	Z
D	E	U	Z	H	F	U	F	R	E	S	H	Y	K
Z	L	K	R	S	L	C	I	S	E	G	M	A	N
K	O	I	O	D	R	E	A	M	D	A	T	F	B
L	H	C	M	M	D	E	I	L	E	A	R	I	A
I	W	O	A	H	S	S	Z	R	C	I	L	V	L
M	B	O	C	C	O	N	C	I	N	I	S	A	L
G	R	K	S	F	R	G	M	D	T	T	U	N	S
W	H	I	T	E	O	U	L	E	R	E	Y	M	R
H	G	N	F	A	F	E	B	I	L	X	P	D	O
E	O	G	T	F	S	F	N	B	T	T	Y	P	V
Y	Q	S	A	S	P	G	Y	J	E	U	S	J	A
S	A	L	T	E	D	E	D	D	E	R	H	S	L
P	I	Z	Z	A	O	B	R	I	N	E	Y	O	F

43

Peach Varieties

BLAKE
CAMDEN
CARDINAL
CLAYTON
CRESTHAVEN
DENMAN
DIXIGEM
ELBERTA
ENCORE
FAYETTE
GOLDCREST
HARKEN
IDLEWILD
J.H. HALE
KEYSTONE
LAGOLD
MADISON
MAJESTIC
MONROE
NORMAN
PARADE
PEKIN
RANGER
RUBIRED
SENTINEL
SENTRY
STARLIGHT
TOPAZ
TROY

A P R U B I R E D M N L Z M

D T A N K E Y S T O N E A L

E O R N O M R H T T N J P L

N N G E J S G Y C C E E O T

M E U O B I A A O S K Y T R

A V X X L L M R T A R J A K

N A L R C D E I L A A H C F

N H A E E I C B U X H H A Q

O T U N N X D R E G N A R N

S S R J V I D L E W I L D I

I E E O N G T H O S U E I K

D R M K Y E M N Z G T Q N E

A C N O R M A N E D A R A P

M U B F Y R T N E S G L L I

44 Have a Safe Summer

USE HYDROCORTISONE to TREAT INFLAMMATION from SUNBURN. WHEN it BEGINS to HEAL, use CALAMINE LOTION to stop the ITCH. FOR POISON IVY, CLEAN the affected AREA with RUBBING ALCOHOL to get rid OF OIL, then WASH with SOAP and WATER. A RASH will DEVELOP A DAY OR TWO LATER. AGAIN, APPLY hydrocortisone.

H	V	N	O	R	T	W	O	R	H	P	T	U	V
F	Y	T	O	F	R	C	N	C	B	A	A	N	L
Q	K	D	Q	S	O	R	T	R	P	R	G	X	A
W	W	M	R	P	I	I	E	P	U	G	A	N	T
A	A	L	C	O	H	O	L	T	C	B	I	E	E
X	D	K	H	L	C	Y	P	G	A	C	N	S	R
N	N	A	Y	E	N	O	A	C	L	W	L	U	A
H	G	E	Y	V	N	T	R	E	A	T	B	H	S
R	E	R	H	E	I	B	A	T	M	B	B	S	P
N	O	A	H	D	E	N	E	F	I	X	N	A	R
F	P	W	L	G	J	J	Q	N	N	S	L	R	Z
J	N	O	I	T	O	L	G	I	E	S	O	A	P
S	I	N	O	I	T	A	M	M	A	L	F	N	I
H	S	A	W	D	T	G	K	A	F	B	X	E	E

45

Get a Hug, Give a Hug

ACKNOWLEDGE
AFFECTION
ARMS
ATTENTIVE
CLOSE
COMFORT
CONTACT
CUDDLE
EMBRACE
EMOTIONAL
EMPATHY
EXPRESS
FRIENDLY
GESTURE
GOOD-BYE
GREETING
HOLD
JOIN
KIND
LOVING
OPEN
REACH OUT
RELAX
SMILE
SQUEEZE
SUPPORT
SURROUND
TOUCH
WARM
WELCOME

E	X	A	G	S	A	W	S	Q	U	E	E	Z	E
E	M	O	V	N	S	L	U	D	M	L	G	T	B
C	L	O	S	E	I	E	R	F	A	H	A	R	G
A	S	G	C	J	E	V	R	N	D	O	W	O	E
R	C	Q	N	L	O	I	O	P	J	L	O	F	H
B	Z	K	D	I	E	I	U	L	X	D	R	M	E
M	A	D	N	N	T	W	N	N	B	E	T	O	V
E	U	R	D	O	A	E	D	Y	L	K	R	C	I
C	Q	L	M	R	W	R	E	A	C	H	O	U	T
Y	Y	E	M	S	W	L	X	R	C	S	P	D	N
N	Y	H	T	A	P	M	E	U	G	M	P	N	E
T	C	A	T	N	O	C	O	D	X	I	U	I	T
Q	R	A	E	R	U	T	S	E	G	L	S	K	T
W	H	O	P	E	N	O	I	T	C	E	F	F	A

46 Pleasing Aromas

AMBER
BALM
BERGAMOT
BERRIES
BLOOM
BOUQUET
BOUTONNIERE
CANDLES
CARNATION
ESSENCE
FLOWERS
FRAGRANT
GARLAND
HYACINTH
INCENSE
IRON
JASMINE
LOTION
PERFUME
POSY
POTPOURRI
ROSE
SACHET
SAVOR
SHAMPOO
SMOKY
SPICY
SPRITZ
SWEET
TRACE
VIOLET
WOODSY
WREATH

N	T	T	H	T	A	E	R	W	F	E	T	Y	R
S	E	E	I	H	S	M	G	A	R	L	A	N	D
E	U	L	H	O	Y	J	B	E	A	Y	N	R	S
C	Q	O	R	C	A	A	I	E	G	O	O	E	S
N	U	I	M	S	A	N	C	B	R	V	L	W	S
E	O	V	M	T	N	S	E	I	A	D	E	B	E
S	B	I	P	O	R	R	E	S	N	E	C	N	I
S	N	B	T	E	G	A	N	A	T	T	P	Y	R
E	W	U	W	A	R	Y	C	O	G	V	H	C	R
B	O	O	M	B	N	F	S	E	I	V	M	I	E
B	L	O	O	I	R	R	U	O	P	T	O	P	B
F	T	G	H	D	S	H	A	M	P	O	O	S	X
Z	T	I	R	P	S	X	N	C	E	E	L	L	N
M	S	S	M	O	K	Y	F	M	L	A	B	Z	T

47 Pudding Parfaits

2 CUPS
COLD milk;
1 (3.4 oz.) PACKAGE
INSTANT vanilla
PUDDING MIX;
1 (21 oz.) CAN
CHERRY
PIE filling;
1 cup GRANOLA
CEREAL;
WHIPPED topping
(OPTIONAL).
In MIXING
BOWL,
BEAT
MILK AND pudding mix
on LOW
SPEED for
two MINUTES
or until THICKENED.
REFRIGERATE
FOR 10 minutes.
SPOON
HALF of
THE PUDDING
INTO four
PARFAIT
GLASSES.
Top EACH with 3 tbsp.
FILLING and
2 TBSP. granola.
REPEAT
LAYERS.
GARNISH if
DESIRED with
whipped CREAM.

F	J	M	N	C	L	T	A	E	P	E	R	M	D
L	A	E	R	E	C	H	E	R	R	Y	I	E	E
A	A	E	O	P	T	I	O	N	A	L	S	T	N
H	A	Y	P	W	P	C	T	A	K	I	A	N	E
M	S	L	E	U	O	O	D	A	R	R	O	A	K
S	A	I	O	R	D	L	N	E	E	O	M	T	C
E	F	U	N	N	S	D	D	G	P	B	I	S	I
T	I	A	F	R	A	P	I	S	C	P	X	N	H
U	L	W	O	B	A	R	E	N	H	A	I	I	T
N	L	F	O	C	F	G	G	E	G	Q	N	H	U
I	I	T	K	E	Q	H	H	C	D	M	G	G	W
M	N	A	R	T	H	E	P	U	D	D	I	N	G
I	G	L	A	S	S	E	S	P	S	B	T	X	E
E	A	C	H	F	I	Z	X	S	K	O	X	K	N

48 Knitting Sweaters

APPLIQUE
ARM HOLES
BUTTONS
CARDIGANS
COLLAR
COWL neck
CREW NECK
CROCHET
DONATE
HANDMADE
JACKETS
KNIT
NEEDLES
PATTERN
POCKETS
PULLOVER
SCISSORS
SEAMS
SEWING
SHARE
SHOW OFF
SLEEVES
TASSEL
TRY ON
TURTLENECK
V-NECK
WOOL
WOVEN
YARN
ZIPPERS

S R E P P I Z Y L E S S A T
E U Q I L P P A Y W L I B F
L S L V Y E B U T T O N S F
O E S N C D Q Z L S O C K O
H A R E H A D J E L W P C W
M M Q C L M O W A G O A E O
R S S K N D I X Z C R V N H
A C R E W N E C K D K R E S
H R V O G A S E I R E E L R
Y O A L S H T G N T S E T N
W C P L A S A R T B E P R S
U H R R L N I A Y V S A U A
O E E M S O P C E O Y M T W
E T A N O D C S S K N I T F

49

Summer Squash

BENNING'S Green Tint
BREAD
BRUSCHETTA
BUTTERSTICK
CLARIMORE
COCOZELLE
COSTATA Romanesco
CROOKNECK
FLESH
FLOWERS
FRIED
GOLD rush
GREEN
GRILLED
HARVEST
HORN of Plenty
LEAVES
POLLINATION
RONDE de Nice
SALAD
SPINELESS Beauty
STEMS
STRIPES
STUFFING
SUNBURST
SUNDROP
TART
ZEBRA Coke
ZUCCHINI

C	O	S	T	A	T	A	I	L	S	M	E	T	S
J	S	E	P	I	R	T	S	E	V	A	E	L	A
P	R	J	N	O	I	T	A	N	I	L	L	O	P
O	E	S	S	E	L	E	N	I	P	S	K	A	E
C	W	T	V	J	R	H	D	Z	U	C	N	R	D
R	O	V	S	G	W	C	B	N	I	R	O	P	L
O	L	C	R	E	Z	S	B	T	O	M	S	O	O
O	F	E	O	E	V	U	S	H	I	R	T	R	G
K	E	O	B	Z	R	R	C	R	A	N	U	D	K
N	D	R	W	S	E	B	A	C	D	Q	F	N	H
E	A	J	T	T	Z	L	W	H	H	E	F	U	S
C	E	A	T	N	C	I	L	K	A	I	I	S	E
K	R	U	G	R	I	L	L	E	D	B	N	R	L
T	B	E	N	N	I	N	G	S	Z	F	G	I	F

50

Mattresses

BOX SPRING
COIL COUNT
CONTOUR
CORE
COVERING
CUSHIONING
DENSITY
DURABILITY
FIRM
FLUFFY
FOAM
FOUNDATION
FULL size
HANDLES
INNERSPRING
INSULATOR
KING size
LAYERS
NO-FLIP
PADDING
PILLOWTOP
PLUSH
QUEEN size
QUILTED
ROTATE
SOFT
SUPPORT
THICKNESS
TWIN size
WATERBED

G	X	S	U	P	P	O	R	T	F	F	Y	Q	G
N	N	G	O	M	S	L	S	O	E	T	U	X	P
I	N	I	W	T	Q	S	U	R	I	E	G	L	I
R	B	Y	N	T	X	N	E	S	E	K	W	G	L
P	P	T	W	O	D	C	N	N	H	Y	N	A	F
S	I	I	A	A	I	E	O	R	K	I	A	R	O
R	L	L	T	S	D	H	O	N	R	C	O	L	N
E	L	I	E	O	G	T	S	E	T	T	I	E	D
N	O	B	R	F	A	N	V	U	A	O	R	H	E
N	W	A	B	T	C	O	I	L	C	O	U	N	T
I	T	R	E	M	C	G	U	K	C	Z	M	R	L
N	O	U	D	Y	R	S	E	L	D	N	A	H	I
B	P	D	I	G	N	I	R	P	S	X	O	B	U
P	A	D	D	I	N	G	F	L	U	F	F	Y	Q

51

Mexican Ingredients

AVOCADO
BEANS
BEEF
CHEDDAR
CHEESE
CHICKEN
CHILES
CHIPOTLE
CHOCOLATE
CILANTRO
CINNAMON
CLOVES
CORN
FISH
GARLIC
KALE
LIME
MANGO
ONIONS
OREGANO
PORK
Chile POWDER
SALSA
SPINACH
SQUASH
TAMARIND
TOFU
TOMATOES
TORTILLAS
VEGETABLES

Z	K	P	V	E	C	R	E	D	W	O	P	C	J
T	K	A	M	S	F	H	K	G	G	D	H	E	C
H	N	I	L	E	T	Q	I	N	A	E	B	I	C
A	L	E	E	E	O	O	A	P	D	R	N	A	K
V	D	B	K	H	R	M	F	D	O	N	L	X	C
O	E	O	U	C	T	Z	A	U	A	T	K	I	H
C	N	G	D	N	I	R	A	M	A	T	L	S	C
A	D	I	E	J	L	H	O	W	L	A	A	E	L
D	E	Q	O	T	L	N	C	U	N	U	S	O	O
O	M	N	S	N	A	E	B	T	Q	Y	L	T	V
F	P	O	R	K	S	B	R	S	D	F	A	A	E
I	S	C	H	O	C	O	L	A	T	E	S	M	S
S	E	L	I	H	C	O	R	E	G	A	N	O	Y
H	G	S	H	C	A	N	I	P	S	Z	A	T	R

52 Mortgage Terms

ADJUSTABLE rate
AMORTIZATION
ASSET
ASSIGNMENT
BLANKET
BROKER
BUY-DOWN
CASH-OUT
CLEAR title
CLOSING
CLOUD on title
COLLATERAL
CONTINGENCY
COOPERATIVE
COVENANT
DEED
EARNEST money
EFFECTIVE age
ESCROW
FAIR market value
FIRST mortgage
FORECLOSURE
INDEX
Rate LOCK-IN
MARGIN
NOTE
ORIGINATION fee
SURVEY

V M O F B E S C R O W D N B
B U Y D O W N H L C U I O R
A T S E N R A E O O G M I O
D M Q E C O E L L R S R T K
J X O D O V L C A C X I A E
U T Z R N A Y M L V C O N R
S E V I T A R E P O O C I G
T K I E I I A T V C S A G I
A N R W N R Z E U R F U I N
B A T Z G A N A T O U M R D
L L S H E A N O T E H S O E
E B R T N E M N G I S S A X
E V I T C E F F E U O S A I
S X F S Y S L O C K I N A C

Eggplant

BAKED
BITTER
BROILED
BRUISED
Many COLORS
COMMON
FIRM
FRIED
GLOBE
GRAFFITI (variety)
GRAYISH
GRILL
HEAVY
ITALIAN
JAPANESE
MILD
OVAL
PEEL
PERENNIAL
PULP
PURPLE
ROASTED
SHINY
SMOOTH
SNAKE (variety)
STEAMED
STIR-FRY
STUFFING
THAI
THICK skin
THIN skin
VEGETABLE
WHITE
YELLOWISH

J	V	S	H	I	N	Y	G	G	P	B	F	G	K
Z	A	C	O	L	O	R	S	P	L	I	G	L	C
B	T	P	K	D	I	F	U	Y	R	T	H	A	I
Y	A	W	A	L	L	R	E	M	Z	T	T	I	H
H	V	K	L	N	P	I	A	B	G	E	B	N	T
T	S	A	E	L	E	T	M	N	O	R	P	N	V
O	V	I	E	D	H	S	I	W	O	L	L	E	Y
O	N	B	Y	H	E	F	E	I	U	D	G	R	O
M	O	R	J	A	F	T	L	P	E	E	K	E	W
S	M	U	W	U	R	E	S	I	T	T	B	P	K
N	M	I	T	L	D	G	R	A	F	F	I	T	I
A	O	S	E	Q	J	F	B	I	O	N	I	H	T
K	C	E	I	T	A	L	I	A	N	R	R	Y	W
E	P	D	J	D	E	M	A	E	T	S	X	L	J

54 Spice Vinegar

START with
four cups of WINE
VINEGAR.
BRUISE
SPICE
SEEDS, add, and
SHAKE
WELL. Put in a
WARM,
DARK
PLACE for two
WEEKS.
Use in SAUCES
MAYONNAISE, or
SALAD
DRESSINGS.
ADD YOUR
CHOICE of
FLAVORS:
SIX tbsp.
MUSTARD seeds,
four GARLIC
CLOVES, six
RED HOT
CHILES, an
OUNCE
OF PEELED,
CHOPPED,
FRESH
GINGER, or
THREE tbsp. of your
FAVORITE
HERB.

L	L	N	T	U	L	C	I	L	R	A	G	B	K
E	C	N	U	O	C	C	W	P	D	W	R	G	T
W	A	R	M	F	H	D	H	D	L	E	I	I	H
M	U	S	T	A	R	D	Y	O	H	A	W	N	R
K	H	D	B	V	Y	O	E	L	P	S	C	G	E
M	T	D	K	O	U	O	Q	R	P	P	E	E	E
Z	D	R	J	R	S	G	N	I	S	S	E	R	D
S	A	E	F	I	H	E	C	N	I	A	A	D	F
D	L	C	L	T	A	E	L	U	A	G	Y	W	T
E	A	I	A	E	K	L	R	I	E	I	E	G	R
E	S	O	V	G	E	B	M	N	H	E	S	Z	A
S	E	H	O	W	Q	P	I	L	K	C	V	E	T
Y	L	C	R	M	J	V	F	S	E	C	U	A	S
O	F	V	S	U	Y	C	L	O	V	E	S	I	X

55 *Money Saving Tips*

DO YOU
THINK
ABOUT what
YOU NEED
BEFORE
SPENDING?
PLAN a
DAILY
BUDGET and
LEAVE the
HOUSE with
ONLY
ENOUGH
CASH to
MEET and not
EXCEED it.
WHAT IS the
DIFFERENCE
BETWEEN
BOTTLED and
TAP WATER?
OFTEN,
JUST
A DOLLAR and
WASTED
PLASTIC.
PURCHASE a
REUSABLE bottle
and a FILTER or
PITCHER
IF YOU
DON'T like
tap water's TASTE.

I	W	F	H	D	Y	R	B	Y	O	F	T	E	N
D	G	H	O	S	Q	G	L	G	Y	Y	L	N	A
M	E	N	A	I	A	I	T	T	T	B	U	O	L
R	T	L	I	T	A	C	H	V	A	E	O	U	P
E	J	D	T	D	I	I	E	S	P	T	Y	G	Q
H	C	U	B	T	N	S	U	V	W	W	O	H	J
C	O	N	S	K	O	E	P	K	A	E	D	K	R
T	N	A	E	T	R	B	P	D	T	E	W	T	E
I	L	P	U	R	C	H	A	S	E	N	L	U	T
P	Y	O	U	N	E	E	D	C	R	T	B	O	S
M	O	F	K	I	S	F	X	G	S	M	S	B	A
T	E	G	D	U	B	E	F	O	R	E	V	A	T
W	V	E	O	R	E	T	L	I	F	Y	O	U	W
N	O	H	T	R	A	L	L	O	D	A	M	B	X

56 *Stylish Eyeglass Frames*

ADJUSTABLE
BENDABLE
CAT-EYED
COLORS
COMFORTABLE
CURVES
DESIGNER brands
DURABLE
EYE WIRES
GOGGLE style
GRIP
HIGH STYLE
HINGES
LENSES
LIGHTWEIGHT
NOSE PADS
OVAL
PLASTIC
RECTANGULAR
RIMLESS
ROUND
TITANIUM
TRANSLUCENT
TRIANGULAR
VINTAGE

T	Z	Q	R	Q	E	G	O	G	G	L	E	A	C
N	C	S	O	E	N	L	P	V	I	Y	T	M	U
E	O	S	U	Y	C	L	Y	G	A	A	R	D	R
C	L	E	N	D	A	S	H	T	K	L	I	K	V
U	O	L	D	S	E	T	E	Y	S	E	A	I	E
L	R	M	T	E	W	S	N	S	L	H	N	M	S
S	S	I	F	E	Y	O	I	B	N	T	G	U	Y
N	C	R	I	O	S	E	A	G	A	E	U	I	T
A	T	G	P	E	R	T	T	G	N	I	L	N	H
R	H	I	P	B	S	T	E	A	Z	E	A	A	I
T	R	A	L	U	G	N	A	T	C	E	R	T	N
G	D	K	J	D	U	R	A	B	L	E	K	I	G
S	S	D	B	E	N	D	A	B	L	E	L	T	E
B	A	Q	U	E	Y	E	W	I	R	E	S	E	S

57

Greek Cuisine

ANISE loaf
ARTICHOKE omelet
BAKED fish
BAKLAVA
BANDIT pork
BRAISED veal
BROILED shrimp
CABBAGE salad
CAVIAR dip
Stuffed CLAMS
EGGPLANT dip
FISH kabobs
GREEK salad
LAMB broth
LIVER piquant
Greek MEATBALLS
Eggplant MOUSAKA
NEW YEAR'S bread
OREGANO chicken
OUZO cake
PICKLED onion
Celeriac PLAKI
PORK roast
Egg POUCHES
RABBIT
Cucumber SAUCE
SEAFOOD salad
SESAME bread
Lamb SHANKS
SPINACH pie
WALNUT torte
YOGURT pie
Stuffed ZUCCHINI

S	L	L	A	B	T	A	E	M	A	V	D	T	E
A	T	R	U	G	O	Y	G	L	V	U	E	I	P
K	E	I	K	A	L	P	G	U	A	C	K	B	I
A	E	G	D	K	R	O	P	S	L	M	A	B	C
S	G	E	A	N	B	P	L	C	K	A	B	A	K
U	P	P	R	B	A	I	A	O	A	N	V	R	L
O	S	I	L	G	B	B	N	R	B	I	A	J	E
M	E	I	N	C	R	A	T	I	A	S	R	H	D
P	S	R	L	A	G	I	C	R	H	E	J	O	S
H	A	A	I	E	C	U	A	S	V	C	O	X	M
E	M	S	R	H	R	H	I	I	L	F	C	O	W
S	E	O	O	A	D	F	L	W	A	L	N	U	T
D	J	K	B	R	O	I	L	E	D	G	M	Z	Z
N	E	W	Y	E	A	R	S	E	H	C	U	O	P

Jars and Jugs

AMPHORA
AMPULLA
BOTTLE
CANISTER
CANNING
CANTEEN
CARAFE
CORK
CREAMER
CRUCIBLE
CYLINDRICAL
DECANTER
EARTHENWARE
EWER
FLAGON
FLASK
GLASS
LIDS
LIQUID
METAL
MOUTH
PIPKIN
PITCHER
PLASTIC
POURING LIP
ROUNDED
SEAL
STONEWARE
STOPPER
VASE
VIAL
WINE

E	R	A	W	N	E	H	T	R	A	E	J	A	P
R	E	M	A	E	R	C	S	Z	L	F	L	E	O
A	E	X	E	L	T	T	O	B	P	L	A	F	U
W	O	W	K	R	O	C	I	Z	U	A	T	A	R
E	J	I	E	P	O	C	G	P	C	G	E	R	I
N	D	N	P	H	U	U	M	A	T	O	M	A	N
O	A	E	T	R	C	A	N	N	I	N	G	C	G
T	R	U	C	Y	L	I	N	D	R	I	C	A	L
S	O	E	F	A	S	I	T	Q	E	L	L	N	I
M	H	W	H	T	N	S	Q	S	R	D	A	T	P
D	P	W	E	C	S	T	A	U	A	L	I	E	O
Z	M	R	Y	D	T	V	E	L	I	L	V	E	S
L	A	P	I	P	K	I	N	R	G	D	P	N	W
F	F	L	A	S	K	C	P	S	J	I	K	B	L

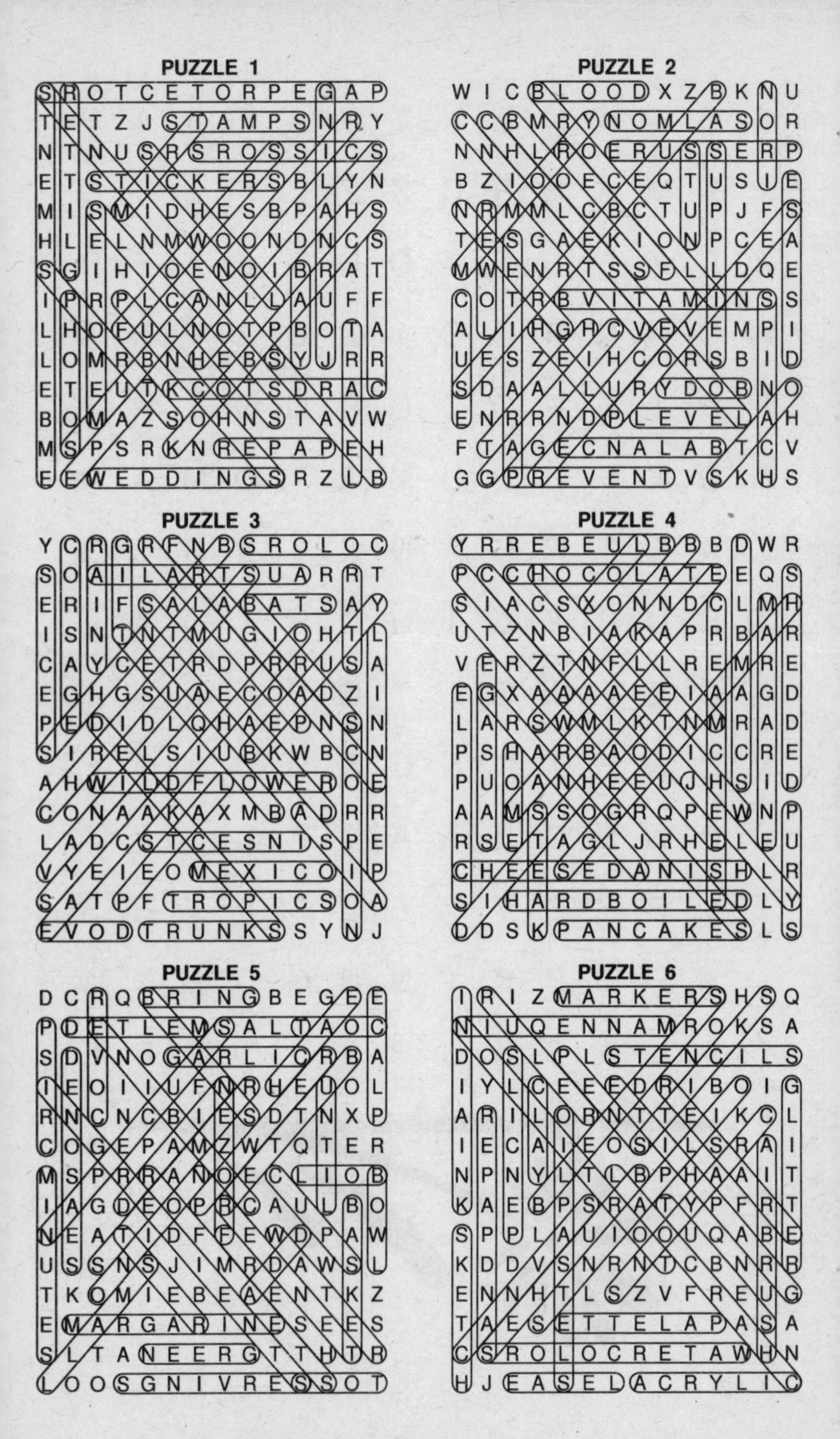
PUZZLE 1
PUZZLE 2
PUZZLE 3
PUZZLE 4
PUZZLE 5
PUZZLE 6

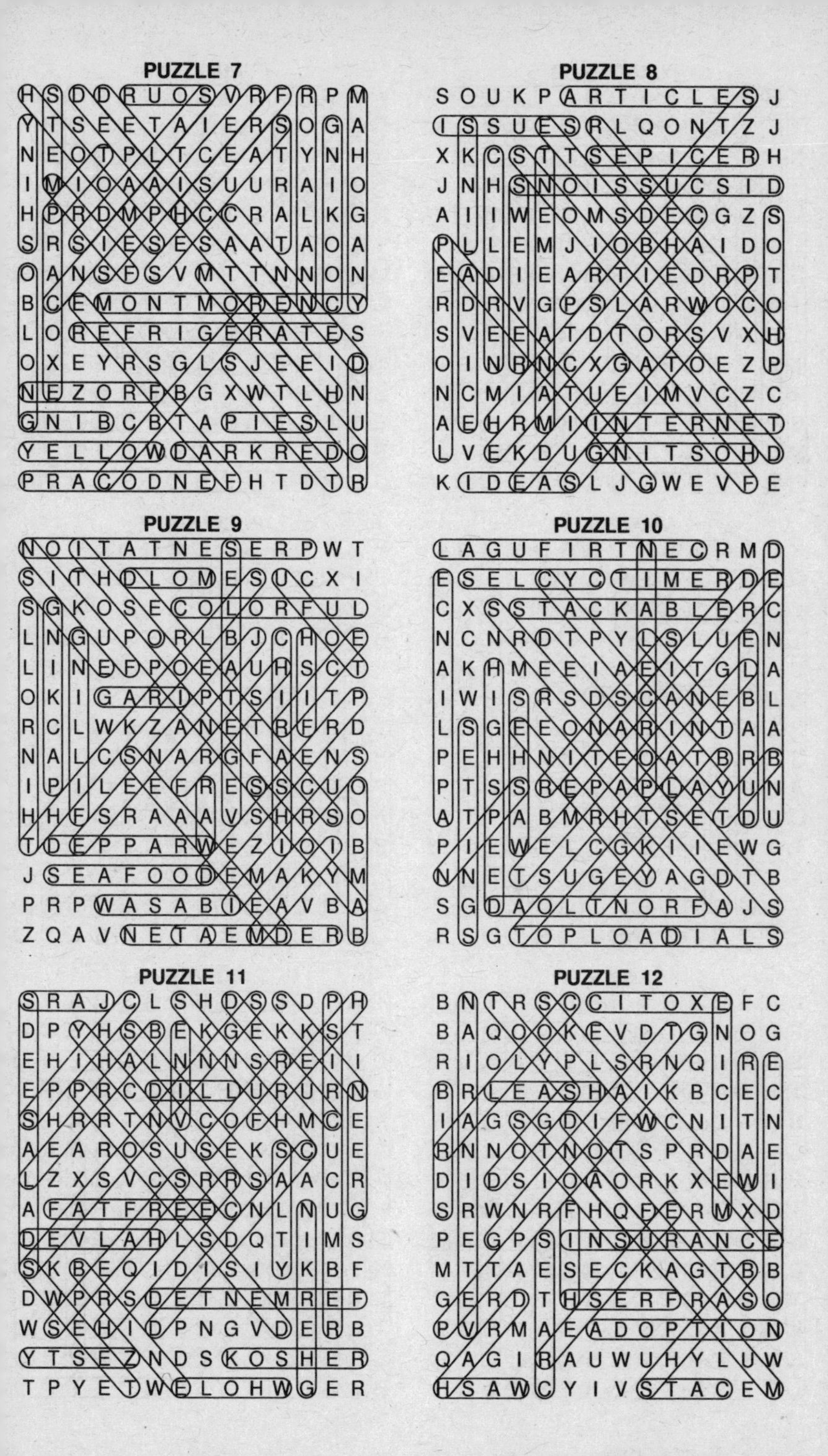
PUZZLE 7
PUZZLE 8
PUZZLE 9
PUZZLE 10
PUZZLE 11
PUZZLE 12

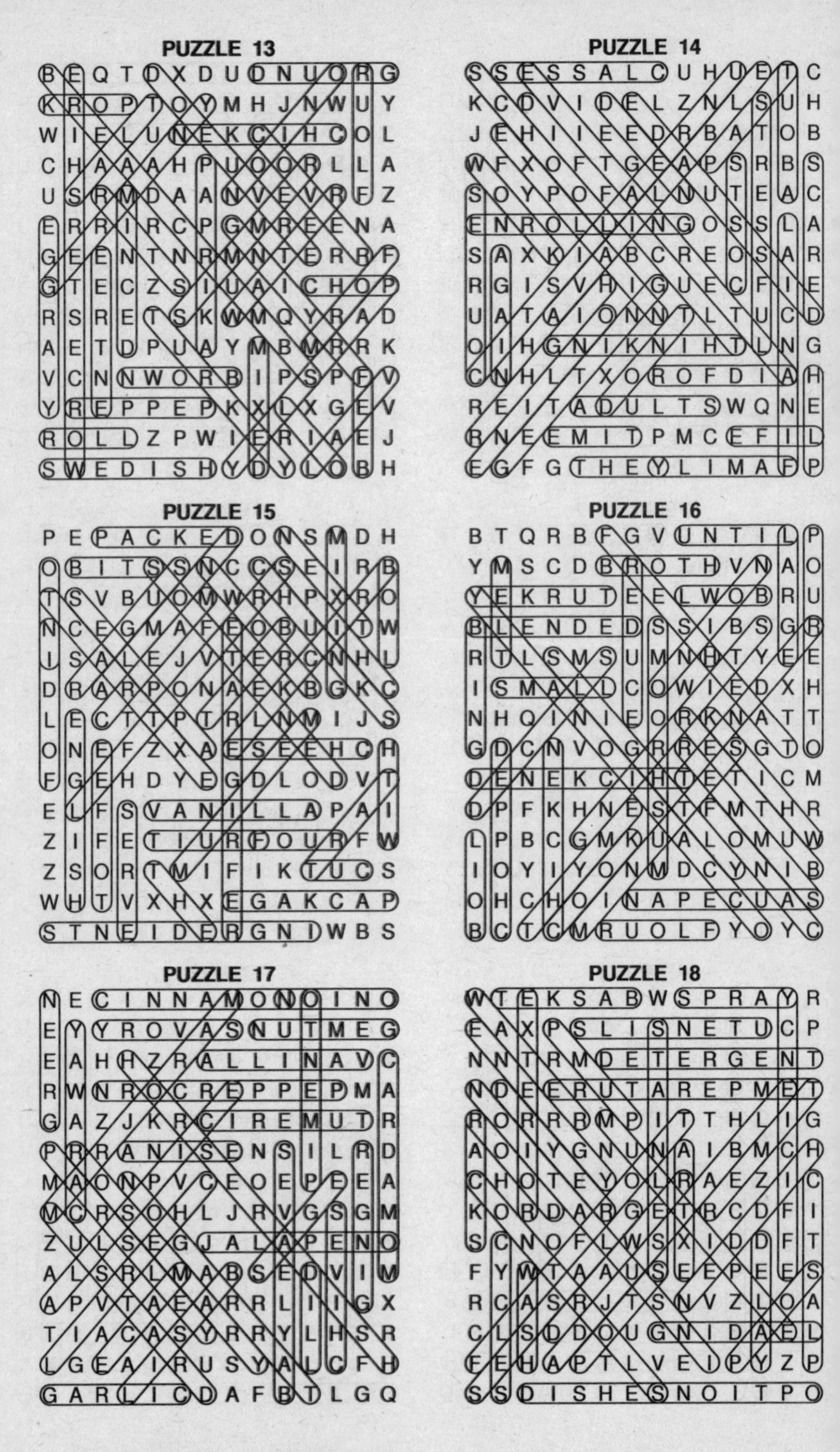
PUZZLE 13
PUZZLE 14
PUZZLE 15
PUZZLE 16
PUZZLE 17
PUZZLE 18

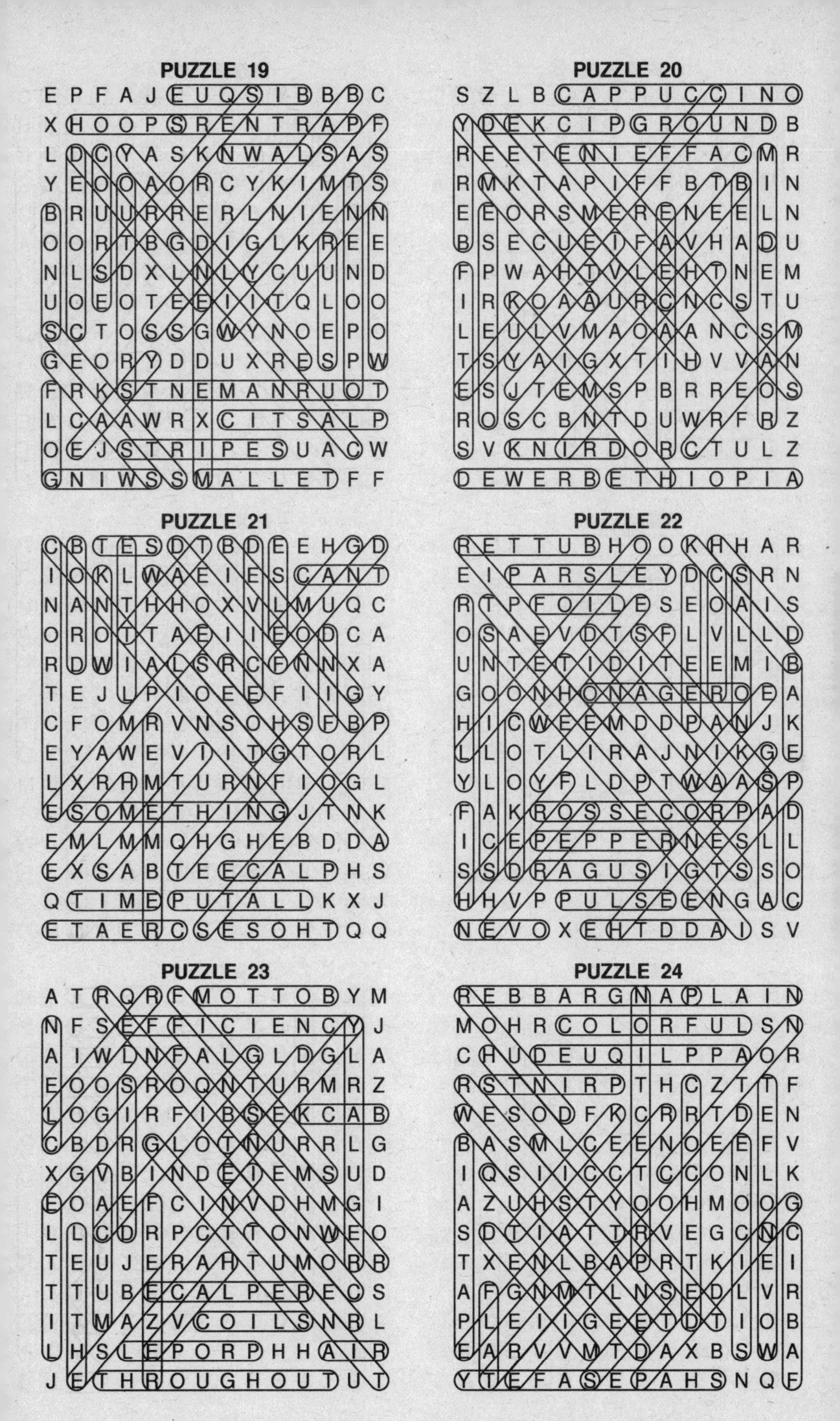

PUZZLE 19
E P F A J E U Q S I B B B C
X H O O P S R E N T R A P F
L D C Y A S K N W A L S A S
Y E O O A O R C Y K I M T S
B R U U R R E R L N I E N N
O O R T B G D I G L K R E E
N L S D X L N L Y C U U N D
U O E O T E E I I T Q L O O
S C T O S S G W Y N O E P O
G E O R Y D D U X R E S P W
F R K S T N E M A N R U O T
L C A A W R X C I T S A L P
O E J S T R I P E S U A C W
G N I W S S M A L L E T F F
PUZZLE 20
S Z L B C A P P U C C I N O
Y D E K C I P G R O U N D B
R E E T E N I E F F A C M R
R M K T A P I F F B T B I N
E E O R S M E R E N E E L N
B S E C U E I F A V H A D U
F P W A H T V L E H T N E M
I R K O A A U R C N C S T U
L E U L V M A O A A N C S M
T S Y A I G X T I H V V A N
E S J T E M S P B R R E O S
R O S C B N T D U W R F R Z
S V K N I R D O R C T U L Z
D E W E R B E T H I O P I A
PUZZLE 21
C B T E S D T B D E E H G D
I O K L W A E I E S C A N T
N A N T H H O X V L M U Q C
O R O T T A E I I E O D C A
R D W I A L S R C F N N X A
T E J L P I O E E F I I G Y
C F O M R V N S O H S F B P
E Y A W E V I I T G T O R L
L X R H M T U R N F I O G L
E S O M E T H I N G J T N K
E M L M M Q H G H E B D D A
E X S A B T E E C A L P H S
Q T I M E P U T A L L K X J
E T A E R C S E S O H T Q Q
PUZZLE 22
R E T T U B H O O K H H A R
E I P A R S L E Y D C S R N
R T P F O I L E S E O A I S
O S A E V D T S F L V L L D
U N T E T I D I T E E M I B
G O O N H O N A G E R O E A
H I C W E E M D D P A N J K
L L O T L I R A J N I K G E
Y L O Y F L D P T W A A S P
F A K R O S S E C O R P A D
I C E P E P P E R N E S L L
S S D R A G U S I G T S S O
H H V P P U L S E E N G A C
N E V O X E H T D D A I S V
PUZZLE 23
A T R Q R F M O T T O B Y M
N F S E F F I C I E N C Y J
A I W L N F A L G L D G L A
E O O S R O O N T U R M R Z
L O G I R F I B S E K C A B
C B D R G L O T N U R R L G
X G V B I N D E I E M S U D
E O A E F C I N V D H M G I
L L C D R P C T T O N W E O
T E U J E R A H T U M O R R
T T U B E C A L P E R E C S
I T M A Z V C O I L S N R L
L H S L E P O R P H H A I R
J E T H R O U G H O U T U T
PUZZLE 24
R E B B A R G N A P L A I N
M O H R C O L O R F U L S N
C H U D E U Q I L P P A O R
R S T N I R P T H C Z T T F
W E S O D F K C R R T D E N
B A S M L C E E N O E E F V
I Q S I I C C T C C O N L K
A Z U H S T Y O O H M O O G
S D T I A T T R V E G C N C
T X E N L B A P R T K I E I
A F G N M T L N S E D L V R
P L E I I G E E T D T I O B
E A R V V M T D A X B S W A
Y T E F A S E P A H S N Q F

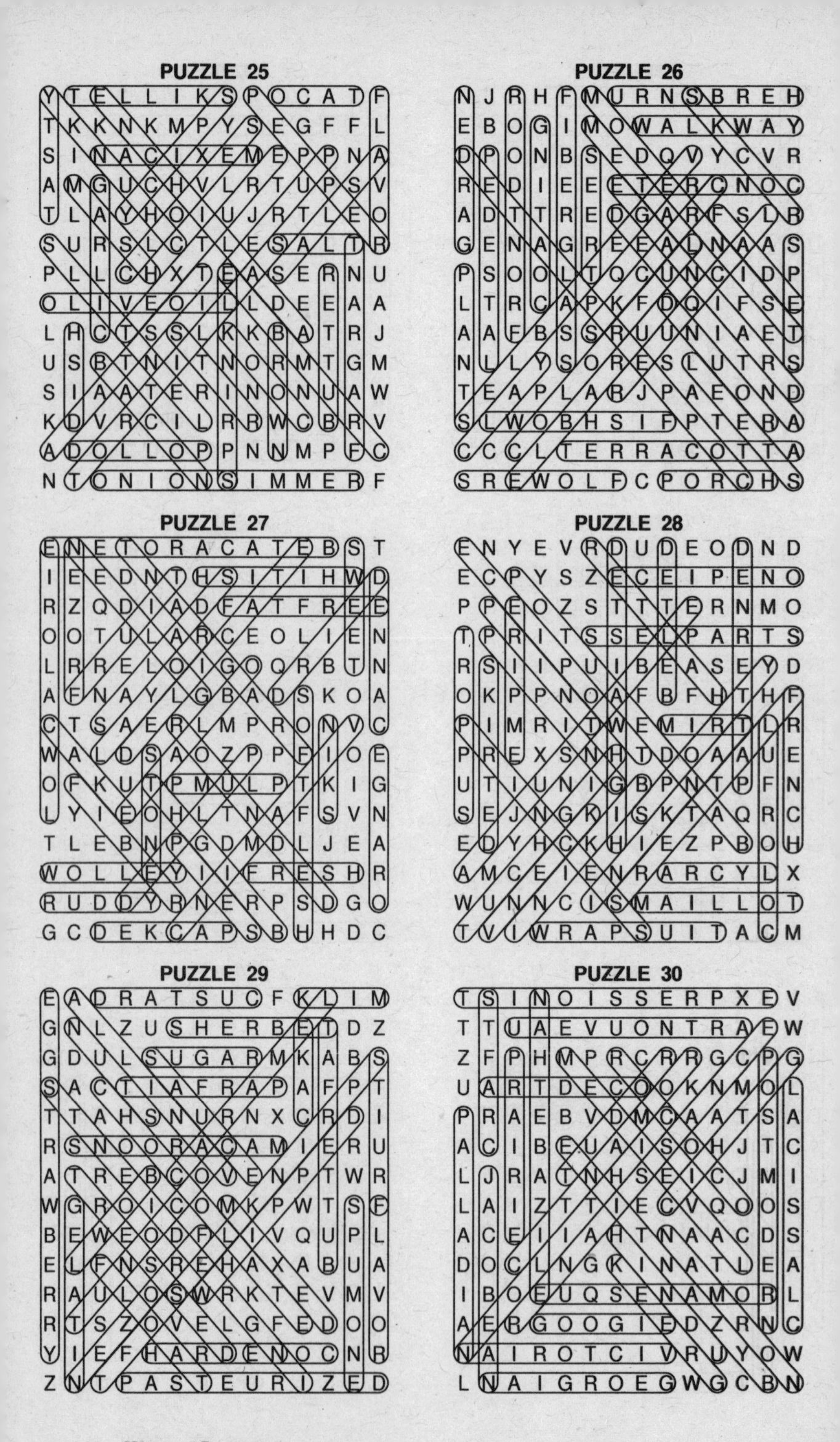
PUZZLE 25
PUZZLE 26
PUZZLE 27
PUZZLE 28
PUZZLE 29
PUZZLE 30

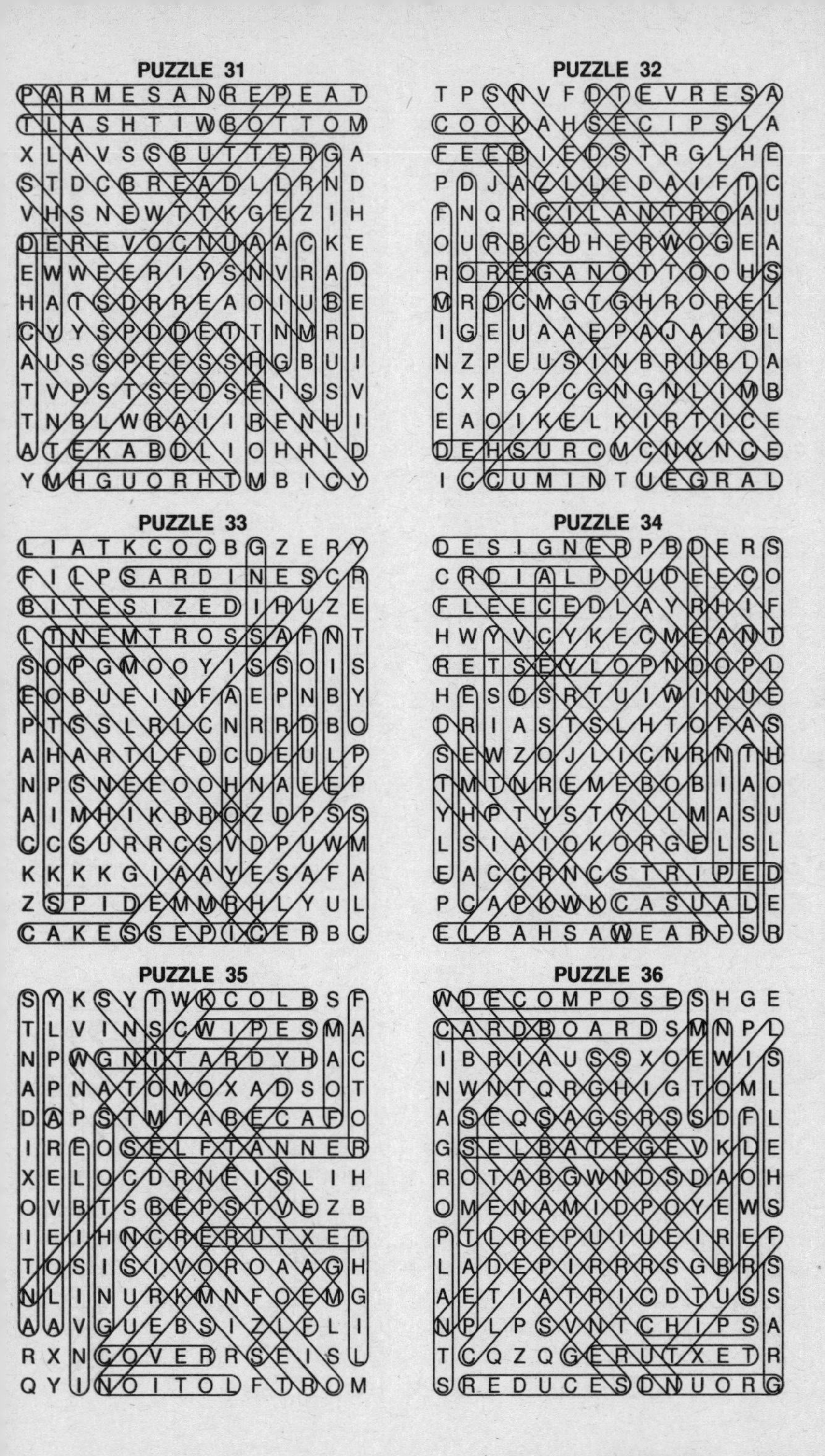

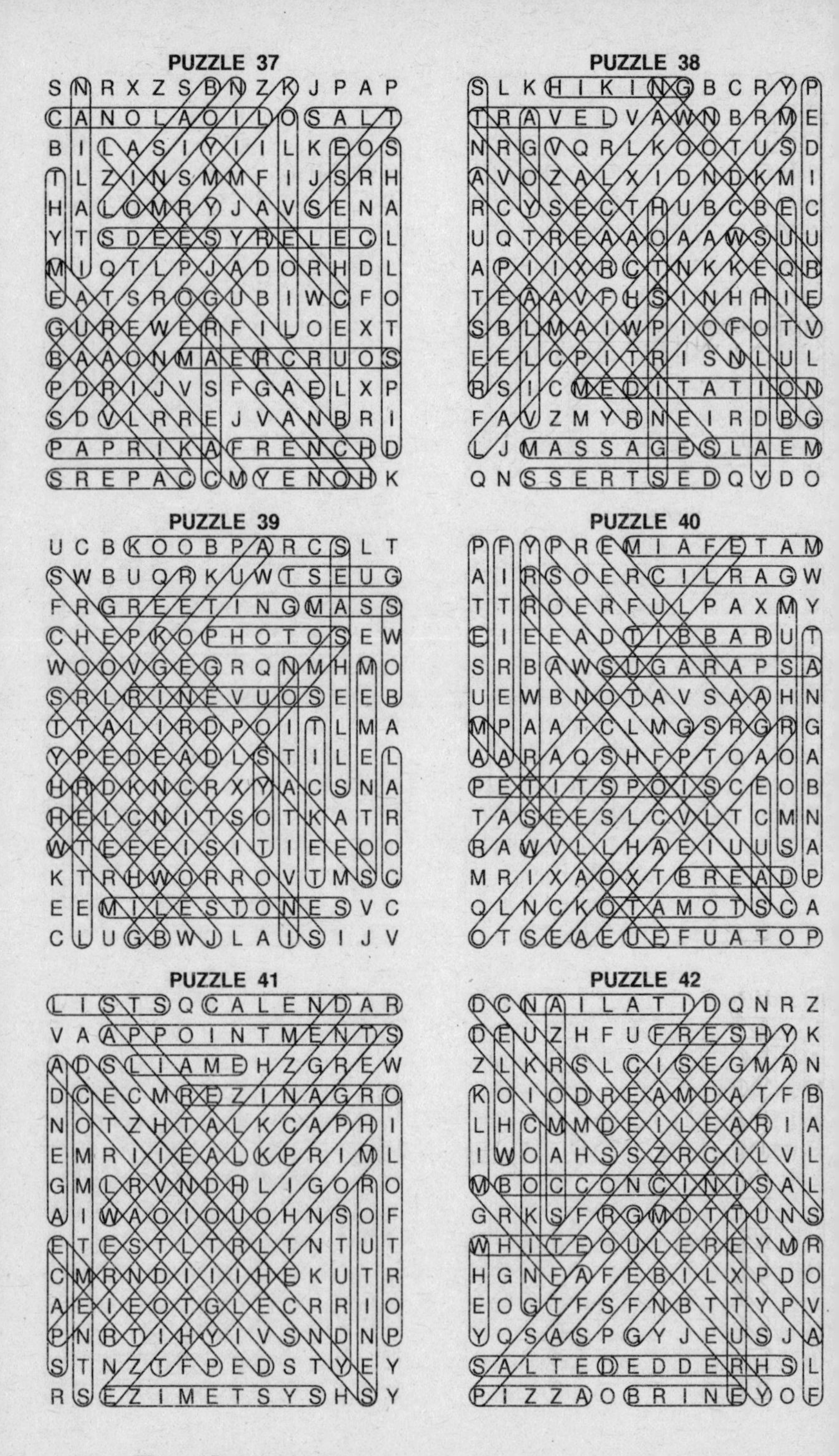
PUZZLE 37
S N R X Z S B N Z K J P A P
C A N O L A O I L O S A L T
B I L A S I Y I I L K E O S
T L Z I N S M M F I J S R H
H A L O M R Y J A V S E N A
Y T S D E E S Y R E L E C L
M I Q T L P J A D O R H D L
E A T S R O G U B I W C F O
G U R E W E R F I L O E X T
B A A O N M A E R C R U O S
P D R I J V S F G A E L X P
S D V L R R E J V A N B R I
P A P R I K A F R E N C H D
S R E P A C C M Y E N O H K
PUZZLE 38
S L K H I K I N G B C R Y P
T R A V E L V A W N B R M E
N R G V Q R L K O O T U S D
A V O Z A L X I D N D K M I
R C Y S E C T H U B C B E C
U Q T R E A A O A A W S U U
A P I I X R C T N K K E Q R
T E A A V F H S I N H H I E
S B L M A I W P I O F O T V
E E L C P I T R I S N L U L
R S I C M E D I T A T I O N
F A V Z M Y R N E I R D B G
L J M A S S A G E S L A E M
Q N S S E R T S E D Q Y D O
PUZZLE 39
U C B K O O B P A R C S L T
S W B U Q R K U W T S E U G
F R G R E E T I N G M A S S
C H E P K O P H O T O S E W
W O O V G E G R Q N M H M O
S R L R I N E V U O S E E B
T T A L I R D P O I T L M A
Y P E D E A D L S T I L E L
H R D K N C R X Y A C S N A
H E L C N I T S O T K A T R
W T E E E I S I T I E E O O
K T R H W O R R O V T M S C
E E M I L E S T O N E S V C
C L U G B W J L A I S I J V
PUZZLE 40
P F Y P R E M I A F E T A M
A I R S O E R C I L R A G W
T T R O E R F U L P A X M Y
E I E E A D T I B B A R U T
S R B A W S U G A R A P S A
U E W B N O T A V S A A H N
M P A A T C L M G S R G R G
A A R A Q S H F P T O A O A
P E T I T S P O I S C E O B
T A S E E S L C V L T C M N
R A W V L L H A E I U U S A
M R I X A O X T B R E A D P
Q L N C K O T A M O T S C A
O T S E A E U E F U A T O P
PUZZLE 41
L I S T S Q C A L E N D A R
V A A P P O I N T M E N T S
A D S L I A M E H Z G R E W
D C E C M R E Z I N A G R O
N O T Z H T A L K C A P H I
E M R I X E A L K P R I M L
G M L R V N D H L I G O R O
A I W A O I O U O H N S O F
E T E S T L T R L T N T U T
C M R N D I I I H E K U T R
A E I E O T G L E C R R I O
P N R T I H Y I V S N D N P
S T N Z T F P E D S T Y E Y
R S E Z I M E T S Y S H S Y
PUZZLE 42
D C N A I L A T I D Q N R Z
D E U Z H F U F R E S H Y K
Z L K R S L C I S E G M A N
K O I O D R E A M D A T F B
L H C M M D E I L E A R I A
I W O A H S S Z R C I L V L
M B O C C O N C I N I S A L
G R K S F R G M D T T U N S
W H I T E O U L E R E Y M R
H G N F A F E B I L X P D O
E O G T F S F N B T T Y P V
Y Q S A S P G Y J E U S J A
S A L T E D E D D E R H S L
P I Z Z A O B R I N E Y O F

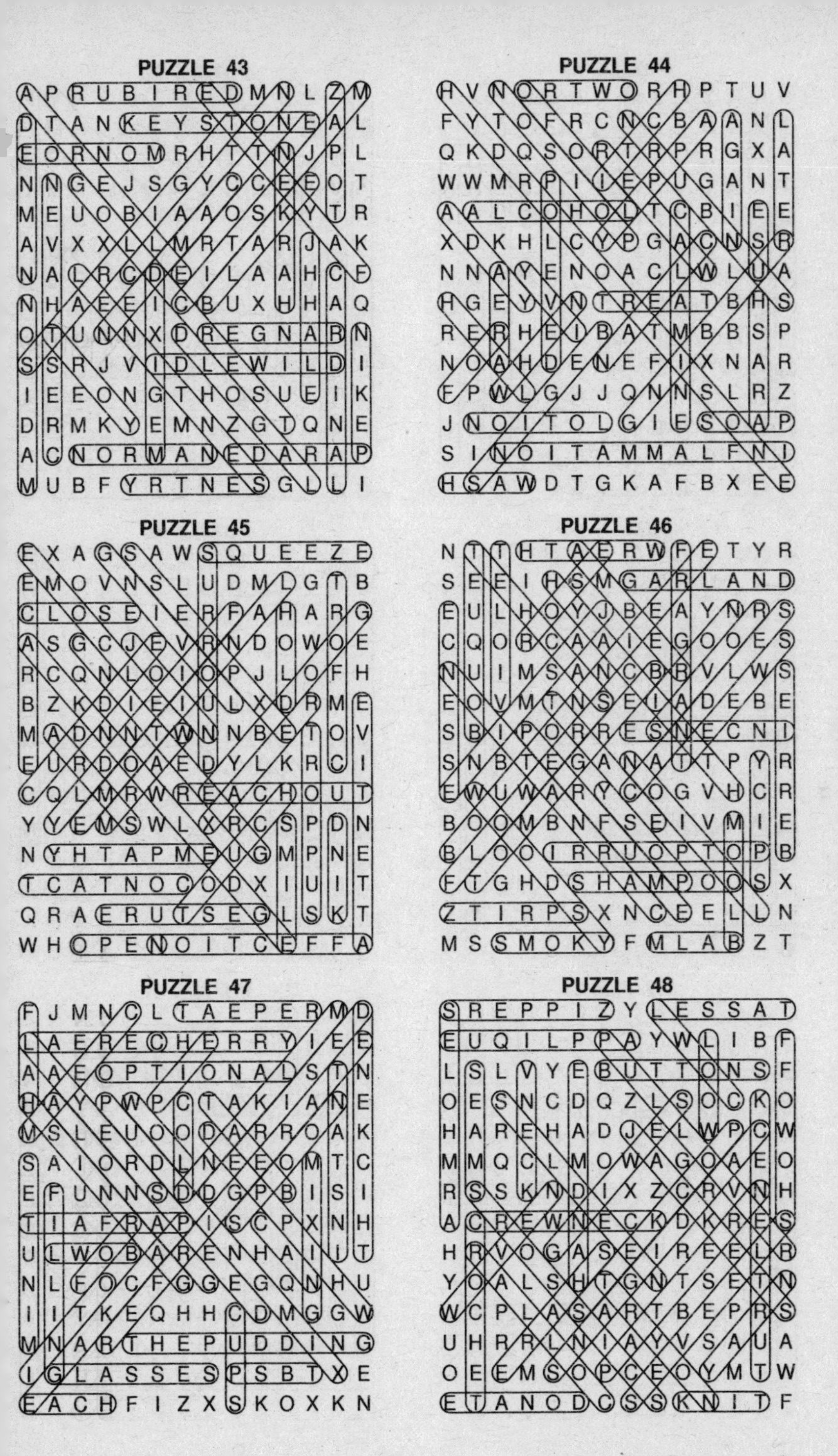
PUZZLE 43
PUZZLE 44
PUZZLE 45
PUZZLE 46
PUZZLE 47
PUZZLE 48

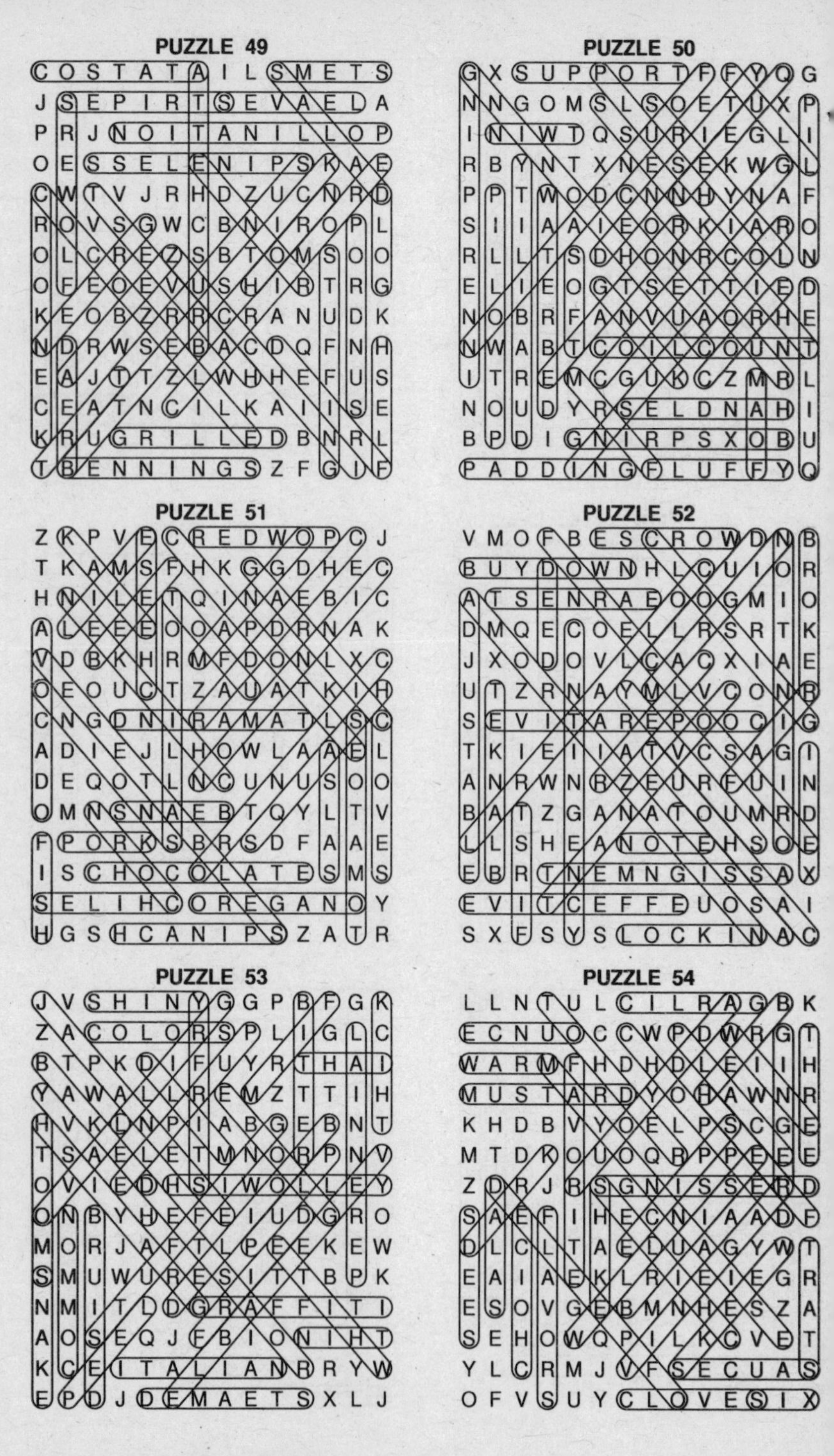
PUZZLE 49
PUZZLE 50
PUZZLE 51
PUZZLE 52
PUZZLE 53
PUZZLE 54

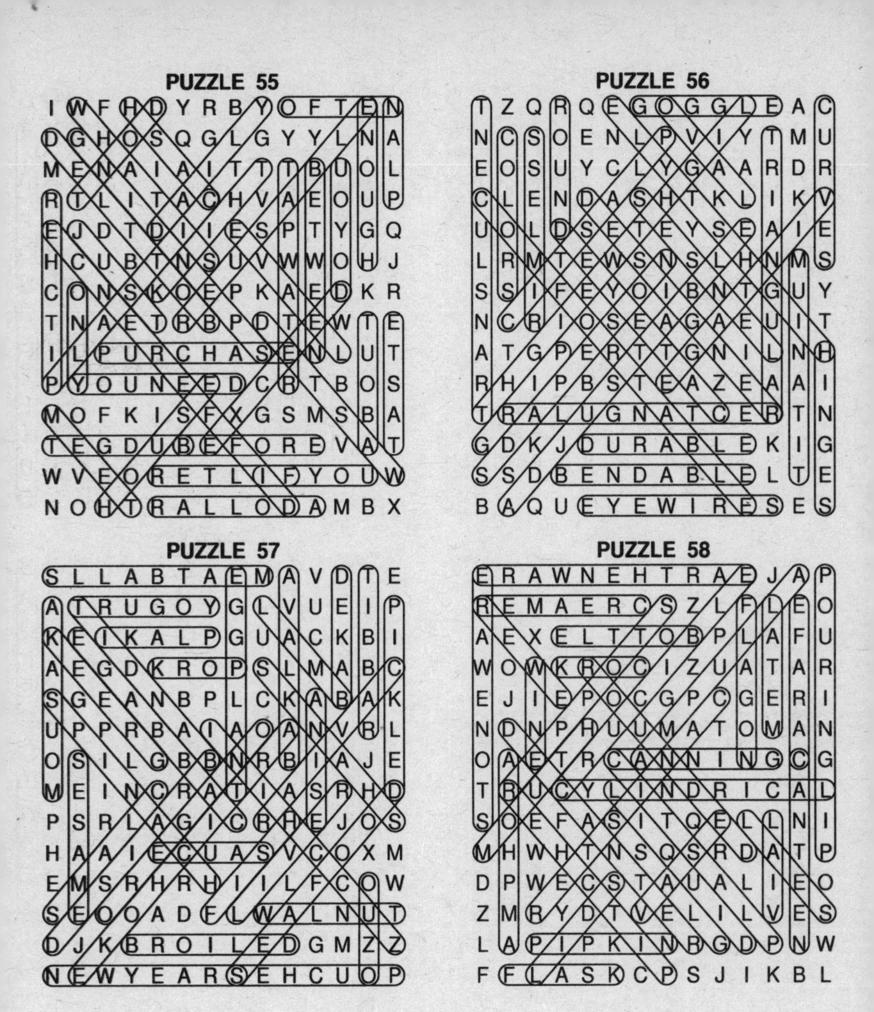
PUZZLE 55
PUZZLE 56
PUZZLE 57
PUZZLE 58